CLASSIC
FILM
SCRIPTS

CHILDREN OF PARADISE

a film by

Marcel Carné

translated from the French
by Dinah Brooke

Simon and Schuster, New York

First printing

Library of Congress Catalog Card Number: 68-27590

Manufactured in Great Britain by Villiers Publications Ltd,
London NW5

CONTENTS

NOTE

This version is based on Jacques Prévert's final shooting script and the finished film. Parts of the film which, for various reasons, were not shot or were edited out of the final version, appear in square brackets.

Three of the characters in the film — Frederick Lemaître, Baptiste Debureau and Lacenaire — are based on historical personages, but the rest of the characters, (except the three authors in the second half), and the action, are invented.

Robert Le Vigan was originally cast as Jericho, the old clothes man, but disappeared at the Liberation when he was suspected of having collaborated, and the part was taken over by Pierre Renoir.

*Marcel Carné in an interview with Marie Portal
before the showing of ' Les Enfants du Paradis '.*

MARCEL CARNE — Right. What would you like me to tell you?
*It is obvious that we have come to chat, only to chat. So what a
strange question!*

*In front of us are some armchairs; we can see the roofs of Paris
through the large open window.*

MARIE PORTAL — About your film!

Marcel Carné, who made Les Visiteurs du Soir, *hesitates for a
moment.*

MARCEL CARNE — Ah well! *Les Enfants du Paradis* is a tribute
to the theatre; nowadays, it would be known as the children of
the gods; they are the actors, the beloved heroes of the public.

We tried to retrace the lives of Frederick Lemaître and Baptiste
Debureau at the beginning of their careers, as well as that of Lacenaire, who was a well-known dandy on the Boulevard du Crime in
those days; but even though these people really existed, the action
itself is imaginary. It takes place in about 1840, on the Boulevard
du Temple . . . known as the Boulevard du Crime, because in
those days, people were getting murdered there . . . and it's about
the stage.

I think the cast was excellent. For my part, I've hardly ever been
so pleased with the actors : Jean-Louis Barrault, Pierre Brasseur,
Pierre Renoir, Marcel Herrand, Louis Salou and the marvellous
Arletty . . .

MARIE PORTAL — I have heard that you had to overcome a
difficulty in order to make the film.

MARCEL CARNE — Yes, that's quite true! And the first was
that the dear old Vichy government had forbidden anyone to
produce a film longer than 2,750 metres, except by special permis-
sion.

MARIE PORTAL — In fact, *Les Enfants du Paradis* is 5,000
metres long.

MARCEL CARNE — A great deal of effort went into making that

film, certainly the most elaborate one that had been made since the war started: three hours long. We had up to 1,800 extras on the set.

But, *Carné adds,* I'll tell you about one incident that was very significant. We were in Nice shooting our big exterior scenes when the Allied Troops landed in Southern Italy. The authorities ordered us to return to Paris. When I went to the Ministry of Information to protest, I was told that they knew from the best sources that there had been a landing at Genoa.

It's unbelievable, but it's true!

The outcome of it all was that we had to stop work for two months, which cost us a mere nine million francs.

MARIE PORTAL — Now, can you tell us what you think about the measures being taken, or at least being discussed, in the cinema world?

Marcel Carné holds his head in his hands, obviously weary of hearing this question being asked yet again.

MARCEL CARNE — No, I can't really. I do want to say for the record that, whatever we may think, the cinema technicians have shown a perseverance, a tenacity and an endurance over the past four years which has to be acknowledged.

MARIE PORTAL — And what about your own plans?

MARCEL CARNE — Six months ago, I said that *Les Enfants du Paradis* would be my last film in black and white. French methods are not yet up-to-date, colour technicians are few and far between. Perhaps it would have to be developed in London. I hope, however, to keep my word.

' L'Homme Libéré ', 3rd October, 1944.

*Jacques Prévert in an interview with Cécile Agay
before the showing of ' Les Enfants du Paradis '.*

*We are soon going to have the pleasure of seeing Marcel Carné's
latest film,* Les Enfants du Paradis. *A film that we have been
waiting to see for a long time. And when we met Jacques Prévert,
who wrote the scenario and the dialogue for the film, we asked
him several questions.*

CECILE AGAY — To begin with, this Paradise, what is it?

JACQUES PREVERT — It is the Gods!

CECILE AGAY — The Gods!

JACQUES PREVERT — Yes, the cheapest seats in the theatre, the
worst, the furthest away from the stage, for the ' people ', that is
why it was called Paradise, in those days . . . the days of the
Boulevard du Crime . . .

CECILE AGAY — And the children, the children of Paradise.

JACQUES PREVERT — They are the actors . . . and the audience
too, the good-natured, working-class audience.

CECILE AGAY — And the story?

JACQUES PREVERT — A story just like any story . . .

CECILE AGAY — Why this story rather than another?

JACQUES PREVERT — Because it happened like that. By accident.
We were supposed to do another story : *La Lanterne Magique.* The
producers were for it and then, all of a sudden, they got slightly
scared . . .

CECILE AGAY — Why was this?

JACQUES PREVERT — Because often producers become slightly
apprehensive about a subject that is out of the ordinary . . . What
if it is a bad subject? . . . Do you realise . . . It would mean
spending a lot of money on ' a bad subject.'

CECILE AGAY — Obviously, put yourself in their place.

JACQUES PREVERT — It's difficult. One has often seen producers
put themselves in the place of the director or the script writer, but
the contrary is very rare. Of course, it's just a question of money.
But let's get back to what we were talking about.

CECILE AGAY — Yes, ' the good subject ' that had to be found.

9

JACQUES PREVERT — Well . . .

CECILE AGAY — And how did you find it?

JACQUES PREVERT — By accident, as usual. It was Jean-Louis Barrault. We were in a café in Nice, and he said to Carné and myself : ' Why not make a film about the Funambules . . . the pantomime . . . the Boulevard du Crime . . . Deburau . . . etc.? '

CECILE AGAY — And what happened?

JACQUES PREVERT — Then we went to see the producers and we said to them : ' Why don't we make a film about the Funambules, the Pantomime, Deburau, etc.? ' And because there had already been a play on the same subject they felt immediately reassured and enthusiastic. It was agreed that Deburau was a perfect, an excellent subject, ' a good subject.' Fine . . . You see, it's all very simple, it was enough to set their minds at rest and so we could begin work and write the story.

CECILE AGAY — Did you take a long time to write this story?

JACQUES PREVERT — Six months. It is a long time, but the film is long too.

CECILE AGAY — And how did you work?

JACQUES PREVERT — Together, as usual.

CECILE AGAY — Together?

JACQUES PREVERT — Yes, all in the same place. With the director, Marcel Carné; with Mayo who designed the costumes, with the designers Barsacq and Trauner: the latter was not supposed to work; with Joseph Kosma, the musician, who wasn't supposed to work either, but who worked all the same, like Trauner, because they wanted to and they knew what had to be done.

CECILE AGAY — How did you work with the musician?

JACQUES PREVERT — It was very easy. As we were all together, I wrote the screenplay, and he composed the music at the same time; we discussed it between us, and sometimes he would play a little melody that could change the course of the action.

CECILE AGAY — How many musicians were working on this film?

JACQUES PREVERT — Three : George Mouqué, Maurice Thiriet and Joseph Kosma. But personally, I only worked with Kosma. Also there were Hubert, the camera operator, and the actors — Jean-Louis Barrault, Pierre Brasseur, Marcel Herrand, Fabien Loris, etc., who came to discuss their parts and who were already

10

familiar with Kosma's tunes.

CECILE AGAY — So everybody got on well together?

JACQUES PREVERT — Terribly well. And when the scenario and the preparation of the film were finished, Carné began shooting; he worked very hard on an extremely difficult job, but it was the best thing that he had ever done. He is a great director and an extraordinarily modest man. I like him very much, and I have already made seven films with him.

CECILE AGAY — What are your future plans?

JACQUES PREVERT — Another film with Carné and a film with my brother, with music by Kosma. I am also working with Paul Grimault on the script of a full-length animated film. Paul Grimault will need at least two years to finish it. The script is taken from a story by Andersen : *The Shepherdess and the Sweep*. It is the story of a very wicked king who is annoyed by a very mischievous bird. There are also some very kind animals, two lovers and a lot of horrid people.

CECILE AGAY — Tell me the story.

JACQUES PREVERT — You can't tell the story of an animated film just like that, it's like an orange, you cannot explain an orange . . . you can peel it, you can eat it, that's all.

CECILE AGAY — Do you like this work?

JACQUES PREVERT — Very much, it is wonderful work.

CECILE AGAY — Naturally, because you are also a poet.

JACQUES PREVERT — Well, yes. Besides, cinema and poetry are almost the same thing.

' Action ', April 1945.

CREDITS:

Production	S.N. Pathé Cinema
Original screenplay by	Jacques Prévert
Directed by	Marcel Carné
Music by	Maurice Thiriet
in collaboration with	Joseph Kosma
Pantomime music by	Georges Mouqué
Assistant directors	Pierre Blondy, Bruno Tireux
Director of Photography	Roger Hubert
Cameraman	Marc Fossard
Sound	Robert Teisseire
Sound mixer	Jacques Carrère
Art Director	Alexandre Trauner
Décor	Lucien Barsacq, Raymond Gabutti
Costumes	Antoine Mayo
Make-up	Paule Dean
Editors	Henri Rust, Madeleine Bonin
Still photographs	Roger Forster
Production Manager	Fred Orain
Administration	Louis Theron
Executive Producer	Raymond Borderie
Orchestra	Société des Concerts du Conservatoire
Musical Director	Charles Munch
Studios	Paris-Joinville (Pathé) La Victorine at Nice
Processed by	Laboratoire Pathé-Cinéma
Shot during	16th August 1943 and 9th November 1943. (The production was interrupted by events of the Second World War in September and October)
Time	3 hours 15 minutes
Process	Black and white
First shown in France	9th March 1945 at ' Palais de Chaillot '; 15th March 1945 at ' Madeleine ' and ' Colisée '

CAST:

Garance	Arletty
Baptiste Debureau	Jean-Louis Barrault
Frederick Lemaître	Pierre Brasseur
Lacenaire	Marcel Herrand
Jericho, the old clothes man	Pierre Renoir
Natalie	Maria Casares
Anselme Debureau	Etienne Decroux
Avril, Lacenaire's assistant	Fabien Loris
Stage doorman, ' Funambules '	Leon Larive
Stage Manager, ' Funambules '	Pierre Palau
Director, ' Funambules '	Marcel Péres
Scarpia Barrigni	Albert Remy
Madame Hermine	Jeanne Marken
Fil de Soie, the blind beggar	Gaston Modot
Count Edward de Monteray	Louis Salou
George, first dandy	Jacques Castelot
Second dandy	Jean Gold
Debt collector	Guy Favière
Police Inspector	Paul Frankeur
First pretty girl	Lucienne Vigier
Second pretty girl	Cynette Quéro
Stage doorman, ' Grand Theatre '	Gustave Hamilton
Director, ' Grand Theatre '	Rognoni
First author	Auguste Boverio
Second author	Paul Demange
Third author	Jean Diener
The policeman	Louis Florencie
Marie	Marcelle Monthil
Célestin	Robert Dhéry
The ticket seller	Lucien Walter
Little Baptiste	Jean-Pierre Delmon
Iago	Jean Lanier
Another dandy	Raphaël Patorni
Arab attendant	Habib Benglia

CHILDREN
OF PARADISE

Part One

PART ONE
THE STREET OF MANY MURDERS

Fade in on a painted theatre curtain, dirty, worn and ragged. Silence. No music. Then knocks and banging can be heard in the wings. The credits come up over the curtain, while fairground music, emphasizing the theme of the film, follows the military knocking. After the credits a very short pause, ended by the three ritual knocks which herald the beginning of the performance . . . and the curtain slowly rises.

Outside it is daytime. Long shot of the BOULEVARD DU TEMPLE: Crane shot, slightly high angle, tracking backwards. A dense crowd comes and goes. Above them all a tightrope walker, not as young as he used to be, goes through his act for the passers-by. He is balancing on the tightrope when the camera leaves him to pick out groups of people sauntering along the street, or hanging about doing nothing. [The camera continues tracking backwards to reveal a group pressing round some other object of interest; then, on the left, on a corner, a whole crowd of people — good, simple people, wholeheartedly enjoying themselves, eating and drinking under the scrubby trees of a small tavern, while they listen to the music and watch the 'artistes'. The sign for this establishment is a primitive picture of three lion cubs holding hands, with the text:

'THE LION CUBS OF THE TEMPLE'
Furnished rooms
Gardens and Arbours
Own food may be brought.

In the background a vague suggestion of the country, a landscape with the paint already peeling.
The period is about 1827 or 1828 . . . it really does not matter.

17

It is the beginning of April; spring is being dragged in struggling by the ear, and winter is still lingering in the streets.] (The part of the scene in square brackets was described in the shooting script, but does not appear in the finished version of the film. However, it is useful to keep it in for the sake of the atmosphere.)

Through the crowd, still in general shot, slightly high angle, comes the OLD CLOTHES MAN, *dressed all in black, a battered old hat on his head, and a bundle on his shoulder. He shrieks out his cry, like a prayer, like a threat.*

OLD CLOTHES MAN : Any old clothes? . . . Any old clothes? . . .
Repeated four or five times.

The camera pans with the OLD CLOTHES MAN *until he disappears into the crowd, and then continues to track slowly along the street . . . the street which is also known as ' THE STREET OF MANY MURDERS '. The whole life of the Boulevard straggles in front of the camera . . . the throng of people, the carnival music, the cafés and theatres, the street entertainers and pretty girls, the elegant carriages, the dandies, the itinerant peddlars, the cheap open-air cookshops, the cheerful fraternity of thieves, the children's merry-go-rounds . . . The background music of the beginning of the film has given way very slowly to the tinkling music of the merry-go-rounds, and the muffled uproar of the street.*

As a carriage rumbles past, the camera pans with it to frame the street in reverse angle shot, stretching away in the other direction. Slow pan, pausing for an instant on a Hercules who is lifting weights . . . gasps of amazement from the crowd. The pan continues, and the camera, still on the crane, tracks forward slowly, towards the front of a circus booth: on the tiny stage, a pathetic MONSIEUR LOYAL *makes a little monkey walk on stilts.*

Track backwards and three-quarters sideways to keep alongside the crowd which surges in all directions. The camera passes a children's merry-go-round, and then, attracted by a roll of drums, approaches a platform where a BARKER *is waving his arms and shouting:*

BARKER : Come on in . . . Come and have a look at her . . . Come and see Truth herself !

Mid shot of the BARKER *sitting on a chair at the entrance to this rather sordid booth, encouraging some passers-by who cannot make up their minds whether to go in. Behind him a young assistant underlines each phrase with a roll on the drums. Behind the assistant a panel of painted canvas shows a naked young woman rising out of a well.*
The BARKER *stands up.*

BARKER *cont.*: Come on in . . . Don't just stand there . . . because once you've seen Truth herself . . . you'll think of her by day . . . *He lifts the tatty curtain to the entrance* . . . and you'll dream of her by night . . . *Roll on the drums* . . . Just have one look at her . . . she's wearing the simplest of garments — she's dressed in nothing but her beauty, she shows herself unveiled to all of you . . . Come on in . . . Come on in . . . Pay on the way out . . . don't let this unique experience pass you by . . .

The BARKER *points with a flourish to the interior of the booth. Some of the men standing around, a bit embarrassed, decide to go in. Others immediately follow them. Track towards the entrance.*

Inside the booth: the camera pans in the rhythm of the previous shot, and tracks backwards at the same time, framing the first group of layabouts who enter the booth and lean their elbows on the edge of the well, staring eagerly downwards. Roll of drums off.

BARKER *off*: Gentlemen . . . you'll never forgive yourselves if you miss this vision of delight . . . voluptuous . . . daring . . . enough to make you tremble with desire . . . no children allowed . . .

Mid shot, reverse angle of the layabouts gazing towards a tub, a crude approximation of a well. They seem a bit disappointed . . . A straggler who has only just come in approaches: obviously not a man to be trifled with — he elbows his way past the others, and he too seems angry and disappointed.

BARKER *off*: Once you've seen Truth herself . . . you'll think of her by day, you'll dream of her by night . . . Come on . . . come and see her . . . Come and see this tantalising vision, gentlemen . . . this is a sight for those who know how to use their eyes.

Close shot, high angle, of the well — or rather, tub full of water — seen from eye level: a lovely young woman, immersed

21

modestly in the water which covers her till just above the breasts, holds in her hand a mirror which she raises above her head. Silent, imperturbable, indifferent to the stares fixed on her she turns gently round and round, lifting her beautiful eyes towards the spectators from time to time, with a distant, unseeing gaze. (Still on page 1)

BARKER *off*: For those who know how to appreciate beauty . . . Come in, gentlemen . . . come in and you will see . . .

BOULEVARD DU TEMPLE, the front of the booth. The cries of the BARKER *fade out as the camera tracks backwards away from the booth to take in once again the crowd and the noises of the street.*

Medium long shot, tracking backwards, parallel with the crowd, who are pressed up against one another queueing in front of a theatre. As the camera passes it is possible to read the sign:

'THEATRE DES FUNAMBULES'

At the end of the tracking shot a pan which ends on a door, above which can be read the words: 'Stage Door'. On the threshold two men are arguing; slight track forward to frame them in a tight close-up. One is a stage doorkeeper, the other a handsome young man with a bright malicious glance, who, although he is dressed in sober, even poor clothes, is extremely attractive and has a natural elegance.

STAGE DOORKEEPER: That's enough! . . . This is the stage door. Yes, yes, I know that little trick . . . but with me you don't get away with it . . . one just wanders in, hoping not to be noticed . . . and then settles oneself down to see the show . . . without paying! And from the stalls into the bargain! . . .

YOUNG MAN: It's not the show I want to see. *The* STAGE DOOR-KEEPER *roars with laughter.* It's the director!

STAGE DOORKEEPER *amused*: The director? The director! You don't ask much, do you? *Suddenly furious.* Well then, let's have it! What do you want to see him about — the director?

Series of reverse angle shots of the two of them. According to the dialogue, the camera is focused on the one who is speaking, therefore, behind the YOUNG MAN *can be seen the crowded street, and behind the* STAGE DOORKEEPER *the bustle of the wings.*

YOUNG MAN *smiling and flippant*: Oh, it's very simple . . . I'd like to see him . . . in fact I'd like to speak to him . . . so that he can give me a job!

STAGE DOORKEEPER *sneering*: So that he can give you a job . . . I see, and put your name up right away, I suppose . . . top of the bill into the bargain . . .

YOUNG MAN *unruffled*: Why not, indeed, sheep's head?

STAGE DOORKEEPER *shocked*: You're not serious!

YOUNG MAN: Indeed, I am, object. I'm telling you now, and I'm a very good teller of fortunes, especially my own . . .*

> *Wagging an admonitory finger at the* STAGE DOORKEEPER, *he takes a step to the left. The* STAGE DOORKEEPER, *worried and suspicious, also takes a step to the left, so that they end up changing places.*

YOUNG MAN: . . . you'll be seeing my name on that poster soon enough . . . and in giant letters too! Frederick, have you got it? Frederick Lemaître . . . never forget that name . . . *with his fore-finger he touches the man's forehead.* Keep it there . . . there, in your weak and wandering memory . . . Veni, Vidi, Vici, Frederick Lemaître . . . remember . . .

> *The* STAGE DOORKEEPER *is dumbfounded, but the* YOUNG MAN *looks up in the direction of the street, and seizes his arm.*

FREDERICK: Oh, look . . . sheep's head . . . look! (*Still on page 1*) *General shot, slightly high angle of the street from their point of view: a pretty young woman, recognisable as 'Truth' crosses the street, and smiling gaily approaches a flower seller whose flowers, laid out on a little cart, make a cheerful display.*
[*Cut back to the* STAGE DOORKEEPER *and* FREDERICK.

STAGE DOORKEEPER: Eh? What? . . . What's the matter?

FREDERICK: You, dust and ashes . . . The most beautiful girl in the world crosses the 'Boulevard du Temple' and he asks 'What's the matter?' *Shaking him, he forces the* STAGE DOORKEEPER *to look towards* TRUTH. That's what the matter is, troglodyte . . . stillborn . . . neanderthal . . . Those eyes are the matter . . . and

---

* Translator's note: FREDERICK'S conversation is larded with puns which cannot always be caught exactly in translation — in this case 'dire' — 'tell', and 'predire' — 'foretell'.

that mouth, as red as a flower . . . and those marvellous legs . . . and the way her body moves as she walks . . .] (The part of the scene in square brackets was shot but cut during the editing.)

Tight close shot of the STAGE DOORKEEPER *and* FREDERICK. STAGE DOORKEEPER *allowing himself to be convinced*: It's true, she's not bad at all! . . . a fine looking girl . . . Do you know her? FREDERICK *still staring after the* YOUNG WOMAN: No . . . Not yet . . .

> *He leaves the* STAGE DOORKEEPER *and dashes off. The camera tracks rapidly backwards and pans to follow him, revealing a corner of the street, the passers-by . . . various games being played . . . Cleaving his way through the crowd* FREDERICK *rapidly walks out of shot to the right. The camera tracks backwards from another corner of the street: the* YOUNG WOMAN *pointed out by* FREDERICK *carries on her way, calm and indifferent among the crowd. The camera continues tracking backwards, now in front of her.* FREDERICK *appears in the background, walking fast. When he catches up with the* YOUNG WOMAN, *he passes very haughtily, without looking at her, and continues out of shot. The* YOUNG WOMAN *walks on, without noticing. Reverse angle shot, still slightly high angle:* FREDERICK *turns round abruptly and retraces his steps, very much at his ease, to meet the* YOUNG WOMAN *he has just passed. As he passes her again, he leans towards her smiling broadly, and salutes her as if they know each other. The* YOUNG WOMAN *smiles and carries on walking through the crowd. Backwards tracking shot of the two of them as they walk towards the camera* — FREDERICK *has once again turned round to catch up with the* YOUNG WOMAN.

FREDERICK *out of breath*: Oh, you smiled at me! Don't deny it. You smiled at me. Oh! It's wonderful! Life is beautiful! . . . and you are beautiful too . . . Oh! You are so beautiful! . . .

The YOUNG WOMAN *looks at him, smiling, but does not stop.* YOUNG WOMAN: How funny, you sound as if you've been running! FREDERICK: Yes . . . I've been running after you!

The YOUNG WOMAN *stops, and so does the camera.* YOUNG WOMAN *astonished*: After me? But I just saw you coming in the other direction . . .

FREDERICK *still out of breath, but debonair, and speaking very fast*: Exactly . . . I saw you a few minutes ago . . . you see what I mean . . . the shock . . . the emotion . . . time to make up my mind . . . and you had already disappeared . . . so !

YOUNG WOMAN *amused*: So?

FREDERICK: So, as I loathe following women, I ran to get ahead of you . . . and, exactly as you say, I came towards you . . .

He gently takes her arm and tries to continue walking. She pulls away abruptly.

FREDERICK *taking her by the arm again*: And now, I shall never leave your side. *She pulls away again.* Where are you going?

YOUNG WOMAN: It's perfectly simple. *Looking him straight in the eye.* You go in your direction, and I will go in mine.

She starts to take a step forward, but FREDERICK leaps in front of her and bars her way.

FREDERICK: Perhaps we're going in the same direction.

YOUNG WOMAN: No . . .

She tries to pass on the right. FREDERICK prevents her by taking a step to the left. The camera pans to follow them.

FREDERICK: Why not?

YOUNG WOMAN: Because I have an appointment.

Again she tries to get past. Close shot of both of them. Cross cut from one to the other, according to the dialogue.

FREDERICK *playing a big tragic scene*: An appointment! Oh, tragic destiny . . . we've only been together for two minutes and already you want to leave me, and why? . . . for ' another ', of course ! . . . And, of course, you love him, don't you, this ' other man '?

YOUNG WOMAN *smiling and shrugging her shoulders*: Oh, me . . . I love everybody !

FREDERICK: Well, then, what are we worrying about? That's perfect ! . . . I'm not jealous . . . But what about him, humph . . . ' the other man '? . . . I'm sure he's jealous ! . . .

YOUNG WOMAN *smiling*: And what do you know about it?

FREDERICK *peremptorily*: They all are . . . except for me.

Again FREDERICK takes her arm and bends his head close to hers. They walk together for a few moments. The camera continues to track backwards in front of them.

FREDERICK: All right, we won't talk about the others any more, we'll forget them . . . we'll forget ' him '! . . . We won't think about him any more. Let's think about ourselves instead, we've got so much to say to each other!

YOUNG WOMAN *pulling away a little*: Indeed . . .

FREDERICK: Yes, we have! First of all I'll tell you my name. My name is Frederick. Now you tell me yours.

YOUNG WOMAN: I'm called Garance . . .

FREDERICK: Garance . . . that's pretty . . .

GARANCE: It's the name of a flower.

FREDERICK *looking at her*: A red flower, like your lips. [*Becoming more and more impassioned he presses her against his side, carrying her along with him*: Oh! Garance! My solitary, my unique, my first and last love! What are we doing here, in this crowd, with all these people keeping us apart? *Lowering his voice, putting on a tone of exaggerated tenderness.* We could be so happy somewhere else . . . anywhere . . . it doesn't matter . . . where we could be alone, just the two of us . . .

> GARANCE *stops. So does the camera. She pulls her arm away yet again.*

GARANCE: What for?

FREDERICK *in a low voice*: Do you really need me to tell you?

GARANCE: No, you don't have to bother . . . I understand everything you want to say before you've said it.

FREDERICK: Well then? . . .] (Shot, but not used.)

> GARANCE *leaves* FREDERICK, *takes a step forward, and then turns back towards him.*

GARANCE: Well, au revoir, Frederick.

FREDERICK *disappointed*: Don't you like me?

GARANCE: I didn't say that, but I've got an appointment.

FREDERICK *put out, but carrying it off well*: Come on Garance, you can't abandon me like this, leave me all alone in the ' Street of Many Murders ' . . . at least tell me when I can see you again?

> *Series of reverse angle close shots. The crowd can always be seen in the background.*

GARANCE *sceptical*: Soon, perhaps? . . . who knows what chance will bring?

FREDERICK: Oh! What do you mean, chance? [You surely can't expect me to run through the streets looking for you every day? Granted, I adore you, you are very beautiful . . . but —] (Cut during editing) Paris is a big place, you know!

GARANCE : No, for those who love each other with such a ' grand passion ', Paris is very small!

With a last smile at FREDERICK *she turns and walks away. The camera pans to follow her. Cut back to* FREDERICK *in close shot; he is obviously crestfallen, but cannot repress a little smile. Shot of* GARANCE *disappearing into the crowd. Shot of* FREDERICK *watching her go.* GARANCE *is out of shot. Suddenly a broad smile spreads over his face. Shot of a pretty young girl walking towards him. She takes* FREDERICK'S *smile as a homage to her beauty, and smiles back at him. Cut to a mid shot of* FREDERICK *from the front; the pretty girl comes into shot, from the right, with her back to the camera.* FREDERICK *rushes towards her.*

FREDERICK : Ah! Yes, yes, you did . . . you smiled at me . . . you can't deny it . . . Life is beautiful . . . you smiled . . .

He takes the young girl by the arm and walks off with her. Both of them disappear into the crowd, backs to the camera.
[A BARKER *off, a few paces away* : Here it is! The only, the unique, the incomparable ' Waxwork Portrait Gallery! ' All the greats of this world, life-size — incredible realism. Come in and see Marat in his bath, Napoleon on St. Helena, Jonas inside his whale, the Duke of Guise's catacombs, the Six Burgomasters of Calais, the Massacre of St. Bartholomew . . .] (Cut during the shooting. After this scene in the shooting script there is a note making it clear that the whole scene takes place against the background of the street music and the noise of the crowd, above which can be heard from time to time the sharp cry of a passing pedlar, a show being given on the stage of an open-air theatre, the laughter of passers-by, or the patter of the barkers.)

Close-up of a shop sign on which can be read: ' PUBLIC LETTER WRITER '
It is daytime. Inside the public letter writer's shop. Close shot of a man who is still young, but whose features are already sharp and bitter. He expresses himself carefully, his bearing is distinguished, even elegant, but in his eyes are fleeting glimpses of a disturbing cruelty. He is wearing a black, well-worn suit but his shirt is dazzling white. He is writing a letter, reading it aloud in a cold, expressionless voice as he does so. The camera moves back to reveal him as the PUBLIC LETTER

WRITER, *sitting behind his desk; standing by a bench on the left is a* CLIENT, *a hulking brute of limited intelligence who is listening with a smile of blissful idiocy.*

PUBLIC LETTER WRITER *reading*: ' My love and my life . . . I have always loved you, and since you went away, time drags as heavily on my heart as chains on the limbs of a convict . . . Come back, I beg you . . . and I swear that never again . . .'

The doorbell at the entrance to the shop tinkles. The PUBLIC LETTER WRITER *stops reading and raises his head, looking towards the door. Mid shot of the door opening. A big tough comes in, blonde and easy-going — AVRIL. He is wearing a flower stuck behind one ear, and half under his breath is whistling a pretty little tune. The camera pans to follow him as he comes up to the desk and stands there listening to the* PUBLIC LETTER WRITER *writing and reading.*

PUBLIC LETTER WRITER: ' Yes, I swear it. Never again, will I raise my hand to you as I used to do.' *He stands up and hands the letter to the client.* Will that do?

The CLIENT, *overwhelmed, looks for his money, hands a coin to the* LETTER WRITER, *and takes his letter, talking all the time.*

CLIENT: Is that all right? It's blooming marvellous, that's what it is! Brings tears to your eyes . . . If that doesn't bring her round . . . I swear to you . . . well, I mean to say, nothing will . . . if that doesn't do the trick.

He exits left while the camera tracks forward to frame the LETTER WRITER *and* AVRIL *in a very close shot. The* LETTER WRITER *is in profile in the foreground. Contemptuously playing with the coin, he watches his* CLIENT *leave. The tinkle of the doorbell can be heard as it closes behind him.*

LETTER WRITER: Poor idiot!

AVRIL *stops whistling*: All the same . . . you can't deny it . . . it's a fine thing . . .

PUBLIC LETTER WRITER: What is?

AVRIL *respectful and sententious*: Learning!

PUBLIC LETTER WRITER *shaking his head*: My poor Avril!

AVRIL *not taking any notice*: It's true, Monsieur Lacenaire. *With great respect.* It's a mystery to me how you manage to think up all that stuff!

LACENAIRE *shrugging his shoulders, very cold*: Enough of this nonsense. Let's get down to business. *He approaches* AVRIL — *the camera following him*. Did you get the stuff?

AVRIL: Oh, yes, Monsieur Lacenaire. *He takes a handful of spoons out of his pocket and weighs them in his hand with a satisfied expression.* And they're solid silver!

> LACENAIRE *takes the spoons, which are wrapped in a dirty handkerchief, and the camera pans with his hand in a very close shot as he puts them in the bottom drawer of a small chest. He rises, and the camera follows his movement.*

LACENAIRE *with contempt*: Solid silver indeed! *He shrugs his shoulders.* Spoons! . . . and a watch yesterday! . . . Pouf!

> *Suddenly* LACENAIRE'S *eyes shine with a different light. Shot through the window from his point of view:* GARANCE *is approaching, the crowded street visible behind her. Cut back to the two men:* LACENAIRE *nods his head and looks at* AVRIL *with pity. The doorbell rings again. Mid shot of* GARANCE *coming through the door, with* LACENAIRE *in the foreground, three-quarters backview, and* AVRIL *next to him.*

LACENAIRE *to* AVRIL *in a low voice*: Well, well, here's my guardian angel. Off you go, Avril, I'll see you this evening.

AVRIL *touching his cap*: Righto, Monsieur Lacenaire.

> *He goes out, passing* GARANCE *as he does so.* [*As he goes, he sings.*

AVRIL *singing*:

> ' Love asleep in the grass,
> Love in the street corner tossed,
> Love is my sweet child found,
> Love is my sweet child lost . . .']

(In fact, he doesn't sing, but just whistles vaguely. The text of the song is taken from the first version of the script.)

> *As he goes,* AVRIL *cannot resist another little salute to* LACENAIRE, *with a wink this time.* LACENAIRE *approaches* GARANCE, *ironic, but admiring, and his voice is still tender — or at least less acid.*

LACENAIRE: Out of your well already, my angel, light of my life?

> *Cross cut reverse angle shots from one to the other, with slight pans to follow their movements; the one who is speaking is always seen from the front, and the other sometimes in profile,*

29

and sometimes three-quarters backview.

GARANCE *smiling as always*: Oh, the well — I've finished with that, and with Truth!

LACENAIRE: Already?

GARANCE: Yes, the audience were getting a bit difficult. You know what I mean . . . 'Truth, but not below the shoulders' . . . they were disappointed.

LACENAIRE: Well, naturally, those fine fellows wanted more. Nothing but Truth, and 'The Whole Truth'. I understand them very well. The costume must suit you perfectly!

GARANCE: Perhaps . . . but it's always the same!

LACENAIRE *more and more ironic*: How modest! And how chaste!
She leaves LACENAIRE, *and still talking goes over to his desk where she leaves her things. The camera pans with her.*

GARANCE: Oh, it's not that! *Turning towards* LACENAIRE *again.* But they are really too unpleasant.

> LACENAIRE, *who has been looking at* GARANCE, *starts to move towards her, then stops, and stares out of the window at the passers-by with an ugly frown. Close shot of his face.*

LACENAIRE: Yes, it's true that 'They' are too unpleasant! *Sighs.* What I'd really like to do would be to get rid of as many of them as possible.

> *Cut back to* GARANCE, *who shakes her head at* LACENAIRE *as she leans against the desk. Then continuation of the cross cutting from one to the other, following the dialogue.*

GARANCE *mysterious*: Still so cruel, Pierre-François?

LACENAIRE *turning his back on* GARANCE: I'm not cruel, I'm logical. I declared war on society a long time ago.

GARANCE *interrupting him with a smile*: And have you killed many people lately, Pierre-François?

> LACENAIRE, *after a pause, turns his head towards* GARANCE *who is out of shot.*

LACENAIRE *with his usual tone once more, ironic and dry*: . . . No, my angel. *He turns to face* GARANCE, *showing her his hands, which are delicate and well cared for.* Look, no trace of blood . . . only a few stains of ink. But it shouldn't surprise you, Garance, to learn that I'm planning something quite out of the ordinary. *He stares at her suddenly with embarrassing insistence.* You are wrong to smile, Garance, I assure you. I am not a man like other men.

My heart does not beat as theirs . . . absolutely not! Has anyone ever humiliated you, Garance?

GARANCE *sure of herself, calm, and certain of what she is saying*: No, never.

Cut back to LACENAIRE, *who has turned round again to look out at the street. He hesitates for a moment, then begins to talk in a low, harsh voice, as if he is talking to himself; he does not move, but stares into the distance, and seems to be unaware of* GARANCE'S *presence.*

LACENAIRE : Nor me . . . but ' They ' have tried, and even to try is too much for a man like me . . . Even when I was a child I was more intelligent, more logical than the rest of them. ' They ' never forgave me for it. *Close shot of him from the front, as he turns towards* GARANCE, *out of shot.* They wanted me to be like them . . . to think like them : ' Raise your head, Pierre-François, look at me . . . lower your eyes ' — and they forcibly fed my mind with books, with old books . . . *Shrugging his shoulders.* Dust upon dust, filling the head of a child. *A pause — and then he starts again.* A fine childhood I had . . . my mother, my worthy mother, who preferred my idiot of a brother . . . and my confessor, who repeated to me without ceasing, ' You are too proud, Pierre-François, you must take a serious look at yourself ! '

Cut back to GARANCE *facing the camera, listening silently. Cut back to a very close shot of* LACENAIRE; *he gives a little laugh, cold and haughty.*

LACENAIRE : So I took a serious look at myself, and I've never wanted to look at anyone else ! *He laughs louder.* Fools ! They left me alone with myself, and yet they tried to keep me away from bad companions ! *Cut to* GARANCE *and then cut back to him.* What idiocy ! . . . But what a prodigious destiny . . . to love no one . . . to be alone . . . to be loved by no one . . . to be free . . .

It is only now that LACENAIRE *seems to become aware of the actual physical presence of* GARANCE. *His exultation dies. He walks out of shot to rejoin her. Close shot of the two of them, him three-quarters front view, and her in profile, then cross cutting according to the dialogue.*

LACENAIRE : It's true that I love no one. Not even you, Garance. And yet, my angel, you are the only woman I have ever approached with neither hatred nor contempt !

31

GARANCE *very calm* : I don't love you either, Pierre-François.

LACENAIRE *apparently unmoved, but in reality bitterly hurt* : Just as well, Garance . . . But why do you come to see me every day? Is it because I have not asked of you what, without a doubt, all other men demand?

GARANCE *shaking her head* : No.

LACENAIRE : It's true, you're not a flirt. So . . . why?

GARANCE : Because I'm bored.

LACENAIRE *laughing bitterly* : I amuse you, I suppose . . .

GARANCE : You talk all the time . . . it's like being at the theatre. It makes a change, and it's so restful!

> LACENAIRE *leaves* GARANCE, *and as he is speaking goes back to his habitual place in front of the window. The camera pans to follow him.*

LACENAIRE : You are not taking me seriously. If I were a vain man, Garance, I would be bitterly hurt. But I have no vanity, I have only pride . . . and I am certain of myself . . . absolutely certain . . . Petty thief from necessity . . . murderer by vocation, my way is already marked out. My road is straight ahead, and I shall walk with my head held high . . . *sudden smile* . . . until it falls into the basket on the other side of the guillotine, of course . . . Anyway, my father was always telling me, ' Pierre-François, you'll end up on the scaffold.'

GARANCE : He was quite right, Pierre-François, one must always listen to one's parents! *She has moved behind the desk and automatically leafs through a manuscript; suddenly she looks up at him.* Hello, you're still writing plays.

LACENAIRE *modestly*: Oh, sometimes . . . when I've nothing better to do . . .

GARANCE *reading* : ' A Bad Example.' *To* LACENAIRE : Is it a tragedy?

> *Pan to follow him as he goes over to her. Close shot of them both by the desk.*

LACENAIRE : No, it's a little music hall comedy, slightly licentious . . . I can't bear tragedies . . . it's an inferior form — all these people who kill each other without hurting each other in the slightest . . . I find it depressing.

> *Suddenly a few notes on a trumpet can be heard; the same tune has been heard vaguely before, when the* OLD CLOTHES

32

MAN *was passing through the crowd.*

LACENAIRE *making a gesture towards the door*: Here comes the Last Trump.

>*Medium shot of the door which is opened by the* OLD CLOTHES MAN, *who enters hunched, chuckling to himself, and cooing hypocritically.*

OLD CLOTHES MAN: Here I am, here comes Jupiter, known as Jericho because of my trumpet, Medusa because of my burden . . . greetings, Lacenaire! *Looking towards* GARANCE. My humble homage to beauty! *To* LACENAIRE: Well? What's happening today?

>LACENAIRE *looks at him, and makes a sign for him to follow. He takes two steps. Medium shot of the three of them: the two men in the foreground, and* GARANCE, *not moving, in the background.* LACENAIRE *takes out the silver spoons brought by* AVRIL *and holds them out to* JERICHO, *who weighs them in his hand, uncovers them, and gives them back. (Still on page 2)*

LACENAIRE: How much?

JERICHO: What about? . . . *He indicates* GARANCE *with a look.*

LACENAIRE *very coldly*: I have no secrets from Madame.

JERICHO *surprised*: Oh, well, in that case . . . *turning towards her* . . . my congratulations!

GARANCE *amused*: Thank you!

LACENAIRE *impatient*: How much?

JERICHO: Oh — twenty francs —

LACENAIRE *furious*: Twenty francs . . . you must be joking!

JERICHO: I'm not joking, but don't forget that I'm also called the Curse of the Poor, the Miser, the Rat. *He chuckles.* Because I'm as mean . . . *very close shot* . . . as a rat!

>*He laughs. Dissolve.*

>*Outside in the street again, a medium long shot of the peeling façade of the* 'Theatre des Funambules'. *On the left, on a small platform, three musicians dressed in the uniform of Polish Hussars make as much noise as twenty devils, while four ballerinas go through a little dance rather like a can-can. To the right of the dancers stands a middle-aged man dressed in the costume of Pantaloon, and in a ludicrously affected manner inviting the passers-by to go into the theatre. On the right again, quite alone and to one side, sitting on an up-turned*

barrel, is a young man with a whitened face and tow coloured wig; stiff as a waxwork, silent, fearful, ridiculous and vulnerable, he sits there like an idiot, obviously 'not all there'. He is BAPTISTE.

PANTALOON *making a grand gesture with the wooden sword he is holding in his hand* : Come on in, ladies and gentlemen, come on in. A franc for the stage boxes if you're rich, and four cents in the gods if you're poor — or momentarily embarrassed.

He makes another gesture. The dancers stop. High angle general shot of the passers-by as PANTALOON *goes on.*

PANTALOON *off* : Come on in, come on in; come and see 'The Dangers of the Virgin Forest,' or . . . *cut back to him* . . . 'The Crimes of Virtue.' A fairylike pantomime, exotic and pyrotechnical . . . sixteen changes of scene, and an entirely new décor . . .

Cut to GARANCE. *A fat* BOURGEOIS *and* LACENAIRE *are among the onlookers. The camera pans to follow them moving closer, immediately behind* GARANCE.

[PANTALOON *off* : . . . mixed with songs, dances, acrobatics, . . . fireworks, pistol duels . . . *The camera tracks in towards* PANTALOON . . . Russian mountains, Scottish waterfalls, and giant African tom-toms.] (Shot and edited in, but cut in the released versions of the film.)

Cut back to GARANCE, *the laughing* BOURGEOIS, *and* LACENAIRE. *The* BOURGEOIS *leers at* GARANCE. *Then he tries to put his arm round her waist, but she, with a smart blow, knocks it away.*

PANTALOON *off* : . . . come in and you will see a fifteen-year-old girl being chased by a lion from the Atlas mountains . . . a forest fire . . . a flight in a balloon!

Cut back to a slightly low angle shot of PANTALOON *and* BAPTISTE *from the point of view of* GARANCE *and* LACENAIRE. *In spite of his dreamy expression* BAPTISTE *seems to be staring at the camera, therefore at* GARANCE.

PANTALOON *raising his voice* : And you will see me . . . me myself, the only and incomparable Anselme Deburau, who has played pantomimes in the harem of the Grand Turk, in the presence of the Grand Turk himself and of his eighty-two Turkesses. *Cut to* GARANCE, *the* BOURGEOIS, LACENAIRE. PANTALOON *voice off* : But the one you won't see inside, rest assured, is this one here . . .

Cut back to PANTALOON, *who points with his sword towards* BAPTISTE *slumped on his barrel.* (*Still on page 2*) BAPTISTE *is in the foreground, still as a stone.* PANTALOON *smacks him on the head with each phrase, punctuated by the laughter of the crowd, off.*

PANTALOON : Because this one can't do anything. He's retarded . . . He sleeps on his feet, even when he's sitting down! He's a complete dope, a poor booby, an incomprehensible good-for-nothing . . . *an extra hard blow on* BAPTISTE'S *hat* . . . and this one . . . unfortunately, this one is my son! . . .

Cut back to the laughing crowd. GARANCE *is not laughing.* LACENAIRE *is watching the* BOURGEOIS *closely. Cut to* PANTALOON *raising his arms to heaven and taking the crowd into his confidence.*

PANTALOON : Here you see the despair of the family, a family of artistes! The despair of a famous father, the cause of his grey hairs. But when I say, my son. . . . luckily I can admit that I'm exaggerating . . . *Cut to the impassive face of* BAPTISTE . . . One night . . . *Cut back to* PANTALOON *who is pacing across the platform from side to side* . . . when the moon was full . . . he fell down . . . yes, that's all! *Cut to quick close shot of* BAPTISTE. His mother found him in a pail of water. That night . . . *Cut back to group shot* . . . I was away . . . and when I came back it was too late.

[*He taps* BAPTISTE *on the head again, still without his son showing the slightest reaction.*

PANTALOON : Alas: Baptiste was part of the family . . .] (Shot and edited in, but cut in most versions released.)

Medium long shot of the façade of the theatre.

PANTALOON : But we aren't here to wash our dirty linen in public. The show is about to begin, and this show is unique . . . for those who, in spite of everything want to hang on to their money, for the skinflints, the stingy, the Peeping Toms — the management, prepared for any sacrifice, is leaving Baptiste — free.

He salutes the crowd, music bursts forth, and the artistes disappear into the theatre.

Medium shot of a group of people staring sarcastically at BAPTISTE.

FIRST LAYABOUT : What a face! . . .

Close shot of BAPTISTE, *motionless, silent, gazing blankly at nothing. Cut back to the crowd.*

SECOND LAYABOUT : Hey, Baptiste, are you asleep, or have you got a pain in your tum?

THIRD LAYABOUT : Hey, Baptiste . . . wake up, we're here!

Cut back to BAPTISTE. *His eyes flicker and then fix on a spot somewhere out of shot. Reverse angle shot:* GARANCE, *the* BOURGEOIS *and* LACENAIRE.

BOURGEOIS : Hey, Baptiste, if you have any little ones, put one aside for me. *He turns towards* GARANCE *and winks at her.* He looks as mad as a hatter, doesn't he?

LACENAIRE *moves closer to the* BOURGEOIS.

GARANCE *looking at* BAPTISTE : Me? . . . I think he's got beautiful eyes!

Series of quick cuts from close shot of BAPTISTE, *to a close shot of* GARANCE, *looking at him, back to* BAPTISTE, *and then back to a group shot of the crowd again. The* BOURGEOIS *is roaring with laughter.*

BOURGEOIS : Oh! . . . Oh! Beautiful eyes! . . . and a lot of good that'll do him!

LACENAIRE *prudently dodges out of sight. The* BOURGEOIS *is still laughing, but suddenly feels in his waistcoat pocket.*

BOURGEOIS *beside himself with rage* : My watch! . . . Somebody's pinched my watch! *He shouts.* My watch . . . my gold watch! solid gold! . . .

Cut to BAPTISTE *watching the scene, then cut back to the* BOURGEOIS *and* GARANCE. *The* BOURGEOIS *is jumping up and down and pointing at* GARANCE. *He hardly knows what he is doing. Slightly high angle shot, as seen from the platform. During the dialogue the* LAYABOUTS *group round in a tight circle, staring suspiciously at* GARANCE.

BOURGEOIS *shouting* : It's her . . . it must be her . . . Yes, you, I'm sure of it . . . *He takes* GARANCE *by the arm and starts to shriek.* Thief, thief!

GARANCE *trying to pull herself free* : Leave me alone. I don't know what you're talking about. You must be mad!

BOURGEOIS : And now she's insulting me into the bargain! *Shrieking even louder.* Thief! . . . Police! . . . Detectives! . . . Somebody! . . .

Several of the LAYABOUTS *take* GARANCE *to one side.*

36

First Woman *to the victim*: You're sure it's her?

Second Woman: Wouldn't surprise me in the least, a girl like that.

A Man *and not one to mince his words*: She's got to be searched! It's perfectly simple . . . eh? . . . Why not?

Close shot of Baptiste *who has been watching the scene, still without moving. Then slightly high angle mid shot of the crowd. A* Policeman *is approaching. Slight pan to frame him facing* Garance *with the* Bourgeois *between them.*

Policeman: What's the matter here? What's going on?

Garance *very calm, pointing to the* Bourgeois: It seems that this gentleman had a gold watch! Now he doesn't have one any longer, and he says that it's my fault. Why? Mystery!

Policeman *suspicious*: Mystery! . . . Yes . . . and, of course, you're completely innocent, I suppose?

Garance: As a new born babe!

Policeman *to the* Bourgeois: And you, Monsieur, are you sure of what you're saying?

Bourgeois *categorically*: Absolutely sure . . . Arrest her.

The Policeman *takes* Garance *by the arm.*

Garance *struggling*: But since I've told you it isn't me?

Policeman: That's easy enough to say . . . *He turns to the crowd.* Were there any witnesses?

Rapid pan in close shot of the faces of the crowd who gaze back at him without replying.

Baptiste *off*: Yes, me.

All the heads turn round, astonished. Close shot of Baptiste, *still sitting there, motionless.*

Baptiste: I am a witness.

High angle shot of the crowd and the Policeman, *astonished, the* Bourgeois *almost having an apoplectic fit, and* Garance *smiling.*

Policeman: What did you see?

Baptiste: Everything!

He jumps off his barrel with extraordinary agility, and coming forward onto the platform starts to mime the scene. Music begins.

Cut to the crowd, astonished, and then amused, and cut back to a medium shot of Baptiste *from the front. The camera*

37

pans to follow him as he moves. He shows, through mime and imitation, what really happened. He mimes the beauty of GARANCE *and the ridiculous advances made to her by the fat* BOURGEOIS . . . *and the music, and the dancing . . . Group shot of the crowd laughing, and cut back to* BAPTISTE *continuing his act. He mimes the fat* BOURGEOIS *splitting himself with laughter . . . an elegant young man with a dazzling white shirt front who sneaks up behind the fat man and steals his watch with a flick of the wrist, while the fat man is still doubled up with laughter . . .*

Cut to GARANCE, *laughing. Beside her the* POLICEMAN *is confused, and does not know what to do.* GARANCE *does not take her eyes off* BAPTISTE *for an instant. Cut back to* BAPTISTE *who mimes the fat man still doubled up with laughter, discovering for the second time, that his watch has disappeared, and crying* 'Stop thief' *as the thief himself slips away into the crowd; and finally the* BOURGEOIS *stupidly accusing the* 'innocent' GARANCE. (*It is difficult to describe in words this long and superb piece of mime.*) (*Still on page 19*)

Cut to the crowd shaking with laughter. Voices shouting. [*Quick cuts, close shots of the crowd.*

FIRST LAYABOUT *clapping*: Bravo, Baptiste!

SECOND LAYABOUT *admiring*: You must admit he's an artiste . . .

THIRD LAYABOUT *to his* NEIGHBOUR: I'm telling you, he's better than his father.] (Cut during the editing.)

Cut back to the crowd from BAPTISTE'S *point of view. The fat* BOURGEOIS *seems to be very embarrassed among the general hilarity.*

POLICEMAN *severely, to the* BOURGEOIS: Well? What have you got to say now?

BOURGEOIS *stammering*: Nothing . . . nothing . . . I've got nothing to say . . .

[VARIOUS VOICES IN THE CROWD: Baptiste is right, you should be ashamed of yourself, accusing people with no proof! Dirty rotter! . . .

Cut back to BAPTISTE *from the front. His mime over, he is once more gazing at* GARANCE.

VOICES IN THE CROWD *off*: Look at that fat idiot. These people who think they can do anything they like because they've got a gold watch!] (Shot and edited in, but cut in version released.)

Cut back to the crowd, and medium shot of GARANCE, *the* BOURGEOIS *and the* POLICEMAN.

BOURGEOIS *embarrassed*: I'm sorry . . . but anyone could make a mistake.

GARANCE *haughtily*: An error, yes! And not a judicious one! *To the* POLICEMAN. So — can I go now?

[POLICEMAN *awkwardly*: Yes, yes, Mademoiselle you're free to go now.

GARANCE: Good — because the one thing I really love is my freedom.

She sketches a gesture of au revoir, and walks towards the platform.] (Cut during the editing.)

Close shot of BAPTISTE *who, the camera panning to follow him, slowly goes back to his place, hands behind his back. Suddenly he stops, and stands rooted to the ground as he sees something: very quick pan to frame* GARANCE *in the crowd, high angle medium shot, from* BAPTISTE'S *point of view. She is coming towards the platform, smiling. She throws towards* BAPTISTE, *who is out of shot, a red rose which she had been wearing in her hair. The camera follows the movement of the flower back towards* BAPTISTE *in low angle medium shot, who catches the flower, gazes at it, tenderly breathes in its scent, and looks towards* GARANCE, *out of shot. Reverse angle shot:* GARANCE *moves away into the hurly burly of the crowd, but turns round once to smile at* BAPTISTE *and blow him a kiss. Reverse angle very close shot of* BAPTISTE, *who seems to be staring blankly into the camera; possibly at* GARANCE; *he lowers his sad eyes towards the flower. Dissolve.*

[*Medium shot, the camera tracking backwards and then panning with* GARANCE *who is walking through the crowd without hurrying, as she usually does. The camera moves backwards, in front of her. She passes the terrace of a café. At one table, his back to the camera, a man is sitting, his legs stretched out under the table. He sees* GARANCE *before she sees him, gets up and turns round: it is* LACENAIRE. *He puts his hand on* GARANCE'S *shoulder from behind. She jumps and stops suddenly. Camera stops with her.*

GARANCE: Not again!

She turns round, and recognises LACENAIRE, *smiling and casual.*

GARANCE : Oh, it's you, is it?

LACENAIRE : Yes, it's me. So, what happened, Garance, my angel, my sunshine?

He sits down again. GARANCE *sits down opposite him, talking as she does so. The camera pans to follow her until it frames a close shot of* GARANCE, *three-quarters front view, and* LACEN-AIRE, *in profile on the right.*

GARANCE : Oh, nothing much, except that your sunshine very nearly went under a cloud . . .

LACENAIRE : Did they bother you?

GARANCE : Yes, a bit.

LACENAIRE : It's always the same thing. The innocent are made to suffer for the guilty. Ah! It's a fine world . . . a noble society . . . and all that for what? For a wretched object that goes from one waistcoat pocket to another, a toy, three times nothing, a bit of gold with a spring inside it! *As he is speaking, he takes the watch out of his waistcoat pocket and plays with it.* And how did you manage to get out of it, Garance, my love?

GARANCE, *front view, close shot, then a series of cross cuts.*

GARANCE *smiling* : A man all in white came down from the moon.

LACENAIRE *also smiling* : And he made everything turn out all right, of course!

GARANCE : Of course!

A WAITER *brings* LACENAIRE'S *drink on a tray. The camera pans to follow the* WAITER.

GARANCE *to the* WAITER : A glass of wine.

The WAITER *moves off. Resume on* LACENAIRE *from the front and* GARANCE *three-quarters back view.*

LACENAIRE *with a change of tone* : And you didn't say anything, Garance? You didn't mention me?

GARANCE : No.

LACENAIRE *staring at her and shaking his head* : Your character really is perfect . . .

GARANCE : I'm discreet.

LACENAIRE : Pity. *Deep sigh.* I'd have been so happy if you'd betrayed me a little, just a little.

GARANCE : Why?

LACENAIRE *his voice becomes harsher and full of bitterness:* Because nothing makes me happier than to discover that I'm absolutely right in despising the majority of men. *Close shot. He lowers his voice* . . . and of women.

GARANCE *looking at him closely:* Women. Really? What harm have women done to you?

LACENAIRE *embarrassed and defensive* : None . . . absolutely none at all!

GARANCE *insisting*: And what have you done to them? To women, Pierre-François? . . . *with an unkind little laugh.* Not much, I'm sure!

> *A short pause while* GARANCE *watches for* LACENAIRE'S *reaction. Close shot of* LACENAIRE, *hurt; he gives* GARANCE *a look full of hatred. Dissolve.*
>
> *Long medium shot of the façade of the theatre. On the right of the platform,* BAPTISTE, *still rooted to the spot, gazes at the flower* GARANCE *had given him. In front of the building passers-by and a few* LAYABOUTS *are still standing around.*]
>
> (This scene only partly shot, and completely cut during the editing, though both Arletty and Marcel Herrand thought on reading it that it would be one of their best scenes in the whole film.)
>
> *Inside the ' Theatre des Funambules.' Backstage at the theatre there is a scene of unbelievable chaos, made up of bizarre props and fantastic sets, among which acrobats, dancers, dwarfs, men with bird heads, devils* [*monks, oriental princes, policemen and nymphs*] (*these last are mentioned in the script but not visible in the film*) *go about their business. Some are putting on their costumes, some are making up, others pirouette on and off stage, or walk on their hands. Still others are resting or trying to snatch a doze leaning against the filthy walls, stained with damp. The Stage Orchestra can be heard, occasionally drowned by the laughter of the audience. General shot of a staircase which leads down from the boxes well in view. The* STAGE MANAGER, *baton in hand, busy and over-excited, rushes down. He scolds two actors who are arguing.*

STAGE MANAGER : Hurry up, there . . . You're on, get moving will you? *The others laugh.* What do you think you're laughing at, you half-baked lot of . . . *The rest of his remark is lost in the general uproar.*

He goes off towards a door which opens to let in the OLD CLOTHES MAN. *Medium shot of the door.*

OLD CLOTHES MAN: Here I am, Jericho, called the Trumpet, called the Horse-Trough . . . because of the drink . . . called the Poor Man's Curse because I remind him of his poverty!

The OLD CLOTHES MAN *comes into the wings and comes to meet the* STAGE MANAGER, *who stops. The camera pans with the* OLD CLOTHES MAN *as he comes towards the* STAGE MANAGER, *then stops on a shot of them both together.*

OLD CLOTHES MAN: Hello, Stage Manager! I've brought your props; here they are, the poor little odds and ends you asked for.

He puts the bundle he has been carrying on his shoulder down on the ground, and enumerates.

OLD CLOTHES MAN: One hunting horn, one blue King's robe, three death's heads, a pair of gold epaulettes, two pairs of patent leather shoes . . . and . . . oh, yes, and a wedding dress.

He holds up the wedding dress, and turns towards . . . Shot of a pretty girl with dark hair, dressed to go on stage, seen from his point of view. She is standing up, leaning against a piece of scenery, gazing straight ahead of her, with a sad, dreamy expression.

STAGE MANAGER *off*: A wedding dress? Hey, Natalie, that would do for you, wouldn't it?

NATALIE *throws him a look of contempt and falls back into her reverie. Cut back to the* STAGE MANAGER *and the* OLD CLOTHES MAN. *Behind them ' ARTISTES ' and* STAGE HANDS *bustle about.*

STAGE MANAGER: It's infectious, it must be. Look at her, she's turned into a statue of salt as well! Oh, it's a beautiful thing, love, it makes you so cheerful!

OLD CLOTHES MAN *curious*: So it's still going on?

STAGE MANAGER: Oh, it's still going on.

OLD CLOTHES MAN: And it's her father who's against it?

STAGE MANAGER: Her father lets her have whatever she wants. It's — it's ' him ' who doesn't want to know about it. And yet he should think himself darn lucky, a chap like that, who doesn't know if he's coming or going!

The STAGE MANAGER *picks up the bundle and starts to walk off.*

OLD CLOTHES MAN : All right. I can see that I'll have to get busy again.

STAGE MANAGER *coming back towards him* : What have I got myself mixed up with. *Shrugging his shoulders.* What's it got to do with you?

OLD CLOTHES MAN *with exaggerated sweetness* : Don't forget that I'm also known as the Kindler, called Rake the Ashes, called the Piano Tuner, alias the Dovecot, because I can't bear to see turtle doves parted. *He smiles oddly.*

He leaves the STAGE MANAGER *and goes off left. Applause from the audience can be heard off. The camera pans with the* OLD CLOTHES MAN *as he goes towards* NATALIE. *Close shot of the two of them. The* OLD CLOTHES MAN *takes her by the chin, smiling.* NATALIE *jumps, surprised.*

OLD CLOTHES MAN : Here, my lovely, let's see your little white hand. *He takes her hand and looks at the palm.* What a fantastic line of luck! (*Still on page 20*)

NATALIE *disillusioned* : Oh! I don't have much luck.

OLD CLOTHES MAN : Don't talk such nonsense. *Still looking at her hand.* Everything will work out all right — it's marked here, in your hand . . . it's a ' good old papa ' who is telling you . . . you will marry the man you love.

NATALIE *with a glimpse of hope* : Do you really think so?

OLD CLOTHES MAN : I'm sure of it . . . it's written here. *He moves away a bit, then comes back.* And don't forget will you, when you're furnishing your love nest . . . *he winks, friendly, but still with an odd expression* . . . that the good old papa has some very nice silver cutlery, not at all expensive.

On these last words, the camera tracks to follow the OLD CLOTHES MAN, *who goes off, still smiling, towards the door. On the way, he passes* STAGE HANDS *carrying pieces of scenery, then at the door he bumps into* FREDERICK *who is coming in. They each make a gesture of apology, and the camera stays on* FREDERICK, *who stares round the wings, at the strange people, the comings and goings. Close shot of* FREDERICK *dazed and excited. The camera follows him, tracking sideways, with intercut shots of what he is seeing — the backstage squalor*

43

and glamour.

Suddenly he sees NATALIE *in the foreground, still leaning against a piece of scenery and dreaming. When he reaches her, close shot of both of them together.*

FREDERICK : Mademoiselle, please forgive me for interrupting your thoughts, but I want to talk to the director, and I don't know who to ask.

NATALIE *polite but uninterested* : Is it about something important? . . . because I warn you, the director is in a very bad mood.

Close shots of both of them, then reverse angle shots favouring the one who is speaking.

FREDERICK *his enthusiasm dampened by this cool reception* : In that case, perhaps it would be better if I came back another time. . . .

NATALIE : Oh, he's always in a bad mood !

FREDERICK : Well in that case I'd better try my luck, don't you think?

NATALIE : All right. Do you mind waiting a minute?

She goes away, out of shot. The camera stays on FREDERICK *who wanders around the wings, the camera tracking sideways to follow him, devouring the picturesque and unexpected sights. He stops beside a group of* DANCERS *dressed as birds.*

FREDERICK : What a pretty theatre . . . and what a marvellous profession, isn't it?

ONE DANCER : Oh, it would be all right if we ever got enough to eat !

Leaving FREDERICK *standing there with his mouth open in astonishment, they run out to the right, laughing.*

The camera tracks backwards and pans towards a door to reveal the DIRECTOR *in a state of high excitement. He pops out and comes towards his daughter,* NATALIE, *who stops him and indicates* FREDERICK.

DIRECTOR : Wants to speak to me, wants to speak to me? What's he got to say? *Points to* FREDERICK, *who is out of shot.* You mean that one? That flippety gibbet?

NATALIE : Yes, Papa . . .

The STAGE MANAGER *enters from the right and calls to* NATALIE.

STAGE MANAGER : You're on, Natalie !

NATALIE *follows him and leaves frame left. The* DIRECTOR *looks at* FREDERICK, *both of them in close shot, face to face.*

DIRECTOR *to* FREDERICK, *objectionably patronising*: Well, young man, and what do you want?

The STAGE MANAGER *comes into shot from the left passing behind them. The* DIRECTOR *calls out to him without giving* FREDERICK *time to reply.*

DIRECTOR: Stage Manager, don't forget the list of fines. Add Seraphin Barrigni, five francs . . . 'Came on stage drunk and fighting.' *Whistles off, coming from the audience.* That's it. They're at it again! *He raises his arms to heaven, as he very often does.* What's got into them today?

Everyone listens to the noises and hooting from the audience.

STAGE MANAGER: I know one shouldn't say it, but they're howling like dogs on heat . . . up in the Gods!

Cut to the Gods: the audience is whistling and shrieking with laughter.

DIRECTOR: Of course, they are, they can smell there's a storm brewing! *The* STAGE MANAGER *exits left. The* DIRECTOR *addresses* FREDERICK, *taking him by the shoulders.* You can't imagine, young man, you cannot conceive how my theatre is torn by hatred and jealousy.

Working himself up into a state of frenzy he starts to jump up and down and stamp his feet, under the astonished gaze of FREDERICK.

DIRECTOR: We are trying to act on a volcano. This is no longer a pantomime — it's a vendetta. They hate each other, the Debureaus and the Barrignis. It's worse than the Horaces and the Curiaces, worse than the . . . worse than the . . .

Series of reverse angle shots favouring the one who is speaking, the other three-quarters back view.

FREDERICK *politely, trying to be helpful*: The Montagues and Capulets.

DIRECTOR: Capulets? Don't know them!

FREDERICK: It's in Shakespeare — yes, Romeo.

DIRECTOR *interrupting*: Romeo? Never heard of him.

FREDERICK: Alas, very few people know and appreciate Shakespeare.

DIRECTOR: Humph! — and what about you? Who knows you?

Who appreciates you? *Abruptly.* Yes — and what are you doing standing here? What do you want? I've been trying to get an answer out of you for an hour!

FREDERICK : I want to be an actor!

> *The* DIRECTOR *raises his arms to heaven and paces up and down in front of* FREDERICK, *who stares at him a bit surprised, but keeps his dignity.*

DIRECTOR *leaping up and down again* : You want to act! My poor young friend — don't you realise you've come to the wrong theatre? Here, we don't act — we're not allowed to act. Here, we have to make our entrance walking on our hands!

FREDERICK : I could do that too.

DIRECTOR *not listening* : On our hands . . . do you understand? Walking on our hands! . . . And why are we forced to do it? Because they're afraid of us. *Working himself up into another frenzy, and coming back towards* FREDERICK *to seize him by the arms.* They know perfectly well, that if we put on plays here, they wouldn't have to bother to open their doors. Those fine, grand, noble theatres, where the audience is bored to tears! They lull them to sleep, their audiences, with their museum pieces, their antique tragedies, their mummies in skirts who bawl themselves hoarse in old-fashioned language without budging an inch, if you please! Whereas here, at the ' Funambules ' it's alive! We jump, we move . . . *almost dancing himself* . . . Fairyland, what? Things appear, and disappear — just like life . . . and then there's the tap dancing, and the fighting, just like life . . . *The* DIRECTOR *takes* FREDERICK *by the arm and drags him rapidly off towards the stage, behind a piece of scenery. The camera tracks rapidly backwards to precede them.* And what an audience! They may be poor, my audience, but they're worth their weight in gold. Look, there they are; up there, in the Gods!

> *As he says this, he points out the top galleries to* FREDERICK, *who raises his eyes. First a general shot of the theatre, then pan upwards to the Gods. General shot of the audience, filling every corner, then slow pan from one side to the other to get a better look at them. They are crushed one on top of the other, and most of them have taken off their jackets. They seem to be having a good time, as they chew their sandwiches and make comments about the show. Some of the young ones are*

*actually sitting on the edge of the balcony. Those at the back
are embracing their companions, but the majority are splitting
their sides with laughter and slapping each other on the back.
Reverse angle shot of the stage from their point of view.
In a very pretty, baroque décor, representing a virgin forest,
the* ACTORS *are miming a touchingly naïve burlesque, execut-
ing all their movements with great speed and precision. Pretty*
COLUMBINE (NATALIE) *is being wooed by a charming* HARLE-
QUIN. *Watching over their courtship are the girls dressed as
exotic birds, who dance a little flying ballet. A* PIERROT *watches
the couple, sighing with despair, and goes out crying. Quick
shot of* PIERROT, *then quick shot of the audience in long shot.
Cut to resume on a medium shot of the stage as* PANTALOON
(*played by* ANSELME DEBUREAU — BAPTISTE'S *father) enters
behind the lovers, with a gun in his hand. (Still on page 20)
Low angle shot of the Gods, where the spectators are following
the action with passionate interest. (Still on page 53)*

A SPECTATOR : Hey . . . look out . . . here comes the old man !

*Medium shot of the stage as seen from the stalls. Shout of
laughter off.* PANTALOON *starts to fight with* HARLEQUIN. *The
birds fly off.* NATALIE *turns round and throws herself on her*
FATHER, *deflecting the gunshot, while* HARLEQUIN *rushes off.
Close shot of* FREDERICK *and the* DIRECTOR *in the wings
watching the show. Beside them* HARLEQUIN, *with the help of
the* STAGE MANAGER, *is rapidly wriggling into a lion's skin.
Medium shot of the stage as seen from the stalls . . .* PANTA-
LOON, *pompous and ridiculous, threatens his daughter. The
' lion ' enters, without* PANTALOON *seeing it.
Quick shot of the audience in the Gods.*

SPECTATORS FROM THE GODS *during the shot and off* : Hey, hey
. . . here he is . . . here's the king of the beasts ! — Yeow ! Yeow !
Yeow !

*High angle long shot of the stalls, from the point of view of the
Gods. A* SPECTATOR *stands up and shouts to the Gods.*

SPECTATOR FROM THE STALLS : Stuff it, up there . . . we can't even
hear the mime ! . . .

*Quick cut, low angle of the Gods; whistles and shouts of
laughter.
Medium shot of the stage as seen from the stalls. The* LION

47

approaches PANTALOON. NATALIE *sees him, but she does not say anything, as the* LION *puts his ' finger to his lips '* . . . *then delicately places his paw on* PANTALOON'S *shoulder.* PANTALOON *turns round, and automatically gives a polite salute, then is suddenly overcome with terror as he realises that it is a* LION *in front of him. The* LION *with a gesture, asks for the hand of his* DAUGHTER *in marriage. More and more terrified,* PANTALOON *gives them to each other. Group shot. Shot of the audience, silent all of a sudden. Cut to shot of the audience from the stalls.*

The LION *triumphantly bears off* COLOMBINE *(alias* NATALIE*), but as he passes under a tree his ' head ' hits a branch and falls backwards, revealing* HARLEQUIN. PANTALOON *recognising him with fury, picks up his gun and advances, while* COLOMBINE *hides her head. But* HARLEQUIN, *unmasked, hurls himself on* PANTALOON, *disarms him, and hits him over the head with the butt; close shot of* FREDERICK *and the* DIRECTOR. *Laughter and applause in the audience.*

DIRECTOR *horrified* : Oh, the wretch . . . he hit him too hard.

FREDERICK : Did he?

Pan to a close shot of PANTALOON; *he regains consciousness and hurls himself onto* HARLEQUIN.

PANTALOON : Oh — vicious beast . . . snake in the grass, you're going to pay for this! *He takes him by the collar and starts to kick him, shouting:* Rally round, friends, give us a hand! He dared to kick Anselme Debureau!

Close shot of the two furious men; others join in. General pandemonium.

HARLEQUIN : Come on, the Barrignis! . . .

Medium shot of the wings, garden side, *as seen from the stage. The* BARRIGNIS *hurl themselves forward.*

Medium shot of the wings, courtyard side. *The* DEBUREAUS, *dressed as Zonaves and Arabs, rush forward in fury, pushing aside* FREDERICK *and the* DIRECTOR *as they go by. Medium shot of the stage from the stalls. They hurl themselves upon each other.* NATALIE *walks off, shrugging her shoulders.*

---

* Cote cour and cote jardin would be slightly precious usages for stage left and stage right, even in the early 19th Century.

Medium shot of the stalls, face to the camera. The musicians, hypnotised, stop playing. Long shot of the Gods; there the audience, wild with excitement, egg on the combatants.

SPECTATORS IN THE GODS : Go on, kill him! Bam! Smash him in the face! Go on! Kill him! *Several times.*

High angle long shot of the stage, from the Gods: on stage the confusion is complete. Different long shot of the Gods, and more shouts.

SPECTATOR IN THE GODS : Go on then, smack him one in that fat mug of his! Bash his teeth in! . . . See you in the morgue if there's anything left of you . . .

Medium shot of the mêlée on stage, with intercut close shots of fists smashing into faces, and people falling down, etc.

The audience, seen from the stage in wide angle shot. The spectators in the stalls are standing up, guffawing. Those in the Gods can be heard, off, howling with glee.

SPECTATORS : Go to it, Debureaus . . . Push his nose in! At 'em Barrignis! . . .

All this is punctuated with whistles, claps, animal cries.

Cut back to big close shot of FREDERICK *and the* DIRECTOR.

DIRECTOR *beside himself with rage* : Oh, the wretches, Curtain! . . . Curtain! Three francs fine for everyone! . . . Get them apart . . . Somebody . . . bring down the curtain . . . ten francs fine! . . .

General shot of the stage in the foreground and the audience in the background. At last the curtain falls. The DIRECTOR *rushes forward. The combatants separate.*

DIRECTOR : It's disgraceful!

ANSELME *picking himself up, very dignified* : What is disgraceful is that this wretched Barrigni dared to hit a Debureau on the head . . . from behind, and in public! *Bowing deeply.* Anselme Debureau demands an apology. *He puts his hat on again.*

The audience can be heard off, stamping their feet and demanding that the curtain be raised.

DIRECTOR : That's right . . . apologise! Come on, Scarpia, say you're sorry and let's get on with the show. The audience is getting impatient.

SCARPIA BARRIGNI *with a black eye; and taking off the Lion skin* : The Barrignis will never apologise . . . the Barrignis will leave the

49

' Funambules ' and cross the ' Boulevard du Temple ' on a bridge of gold! . . . (*Still on page 53*)

DIRECTOR : You can't mean it! . . . *Raising his arms to heaven.* It's not possible! You're not going to work for Saqui?

SCARPIA *throwing him the lion skin* : Oh, yes, we are! And right this minute. *To the others* : Come on, Barrignis!

> *They go out with silent dignity. Cut back to the* DIRECTOR *in medium shot. He waves the Lion skin and paces nervously up and down.*

DIRECTOR : Oh! . . . It's a death blow . . . a plot . . . a disaster . . . *Noticing the* STAGE MANAGER. Stage Manager, quick, a chair . . . *Suddenly going all lyrical.* Oh! treachery! . . . Oh! loathsome cunning! . . . they have stabbed me in the back! *The* STAGE MANAGER *rushes back with a chair.* Thank you, my friend!

> *Cut to* FREDERICK, *facing the camera in close shot; he is listening with interest to the shouts of the audience.*

SPECTATORS *voices off, punctuating their cries by stamping their feet* : Curtain! Curtain! Curtain!

DIRECTOR *with an impotent gesture* : Listen to them! What a tragedy! *Tears in his eyes.* My audience! My beloved audience!

> *Several quick group shots of the audience shouting.*

SPECTATORS : Money back! . . . Money back! . . . Money back! . . .

> *Cut back to the* DIRECTOR *who leaps out of his chair as if he has been stung, the Lion's skin still in his hand.*

DIRECTOR *indignant* : What? Money back? Their money back? that, never! I'd rather . . . I'd rather . . . I don't know . . . I'd rather do anything! . . . Anything in the world!

FREDERICK *off* : Or anyone?

> *The* DIRECTOR *jumps, and everyone turns round to look at the interrupter who comes forward to bar the* DIRECTOR'S *way. Pan, then close shot of* FREDERICK *facing the camera, the* DIRECTOR *in profile, the others three-quarters view, and then the* STAGE MANAGER.

FREDERICK : That's very convenient . . . because ' anyone ' . . . is me!

> *He points firmly to himself, and takes the Lion's skin out of the hands of the stupefied* DIRECTOR.

FREDERICK : Just let me get into the skin of the character, and

I'll show you what I can do!

DIRECTOR *nonplussed*: But . . . my dear young man . . . I don't even know who I'm talking to. Where have you acted, if you've ever acted at all? . . . and what have you acted?

FREDERICK *roaring*: Lions!

He waves the Lion's skin as he puts it on.

FREDERICK: Always Lions. I know the lion repertory by heart . . . The Gulf of Lions, the Lion constellation, Richard Coeur de Lion, Pygmalion . . . I've played them all!

Quick group shots of the Gods and the stalls; the clamour grows louder, with a rhythmic repetition of the words; 'Money back! money back! money back!' Cut back to the STAGE MANAGER who rushes to the curtain and puts his eye to the hole. The camera pans to follow him, and frames him in close shot, as he fusses about. Shot of the audience, seen through the peep hole in the curtain: the spectators are stamping their feet, banging their sticks on the floor, and shouting rhythmically.

SPECTATORS: Money back! It's robbery! Money back! Robbery!! Daylight robbery!

The CONDUCTOR, embarrassed, makes a sign to the orchestra to start playing, trying to drown out the noise with music.

The STAGE MANAGER comes back in a desperate state.

STAGE MANAGER: There's not a minute to be lost! They'll break everything!

Medium shot of the group. FREDERICK is now in the Lion's skin, except for the head.

FREDERICK: Listen to the voice of the people. The Christians are demanding a lion! We mustn't waste time!

DIRECTOR *raising his arms to heaven*: Disaster upon disaster.

FREDERICK: How much . . .

DIRECTOR *interrupting*: Oh! The ungrateful wretch, he starts talking about money already!

FREDERICK: No — I wanted to ask how much time I should spend on stage?

DIRECTOR *shaking his head with a deep sigh*: The shortest time possible!

Close shot of the DIRECTOR face to face with FREDERICK.

FREDERICK: If you say so . . . but I warn you: once I'm on stage it will be difficult to get me off! However, you needn't worry, I know the action: Pierrot arrives . . .

The DIRECTOR, *then the* STAGE MANAGER, *then* ANSELME DEBUREAU, *panning from one to the other.*

DIRECTOR *starting, and interrupting*: Pierrot . . . but we haven't got a Pierrot either! Disaster! It's a disaster!

As he speaks, he walks towards the STAGE MANAGER, *and the camera, as it pans to follow him, comes to rest on the* STAGE MANAGER.

STAGE MANAGER *suddenly having an idea*: What about trying Baptiste?

ANSELME DEBUREAU *who had stayed on one side, taking no part in the argument, comes into shot from the right towards the* STAGE MANAGER.

ANSELME DEBUREAU: Baptiste? . . . Never! Do you hear me? Never, while I'm alive shall my unworthy son appear on the same stage as his father!

STAGE MANAGER: I assure you, just now he was making everyone in the street laugh . . .

ANSELME *makes a gesture of pity.*

DIRECTOR: Were you there?

STAGE MANAGER: I was told about it.

DIRECTOR: Who told you?

STAGE MANAGER: The Cashier.

DIRECTOR: The Cashier! The voice of the people . . . she's got an infallible eye, the Cashier! She never makes a mistake, not one cent's worth! *To the* STAGE MANAGER. Go and fetch Baptiste.

ANSELME DEBUREAU: I protest!

DIRECTOR: And I am giving an order! *To the* STAGE MANAGER. Go on, my friend! Go on, go on. *The* STAGE MANAGER *leaves shot left*. The 'Theatre des Funambules' is threatened with shipwreck! The rats have left the sinking ship! *Pointing to the curtain, behind which sinister sounds can be heard*. The storm is rumbling, the audience is enraged . . . but I am the Captain after God. *Suddenly making a decision*. I am going to make an announcement! . . .

He goes out of frame right. High angle medium shot of the stage seen from the gods. The DIRECTOR *appears between*

52

the edge of the stage and the lowered curtain . . . salutes the shrieking crowd and raises his arms to calm them. Slow pan, in medium shot of the spectators, whistling and shouting in the Gods.

SPECTATORS : Oh! Oh! Come on, bring him out . . . so are we going to have a show or are we going . . . get off the stage, ugly! Shut the windows, he's going to run away! Give us our money back, you old phoney! Give us our money back!

Cut back to high angle shot of the stage: the DIRECTOR *waves his arms and also makes a sign to the musicians to stop playing. The music stops. After more shouting, the audience quietens down.*

DIRECTOR *shouting*: Ladies and gentlemen. . . . Prepared for any sacrifice, the management of this theatre presents today for the first time, and without any increase in the price of seats . . .

Cut.

The next scene takes place in one of the dressing-rooms of the ' Theatre des Funambules *', which is in a cellar, reached by a flight of steps. In the background is a dressing-table with a mirror above it. On the right a wooden bench. Medium shot of* NATALIE *three-quarters back view, looking at herself in the mirror, where her reflection can be seen full-face. Day-dreaming, imagining herself to be alone, she is trying on the wedding dress. Suddenly, she sees* BAPTISTE *reflected in the mirror as well, and turns round.*

Medium shot of BAPTISTE *who comes down the steps without saying anything. He has put on the* PIERROT *costume and looks far more attractive than he did outside the theatre. He is still holding in his hand* GARANCE'S *red flower, and does not seem to notice* NATALIE; *he is day-dreaming as he walks along. Cut back to* NATALIE *who watches him, surprised. Close shot of* BAPTISTE'S *hands holding the flower, and then slow tilt up to his face still in white make-up; then the camera tracks backwards in front of* BAPTISTE, *but moving more rapidly than he does, stopping when he sits down on the wooden bench. He sits there without speaking a word; in fact, he hardly seems to be there at all.* NATALIE *comes into shot, stops just in front of him, and stares at him with gentle insistence; she is now*

57

facing the camera standing, while he is three-quarters back view, sitting. (Still on page 54)

NATALIE : What's the matter, Baptiste?

BAPTISTE *very quiet, still in his dream* : Nothing, why?

NATALIE : Yes! . . . Yes, something has happened!

> BAPTISTE *shrugs his shoulders nonchalantly.* NATALIE *comes closer and sits at his feet, resting her cheek against his thigh.*

NATALIE : Something has happened! . . . You're so handsome!

> *The camera moves forward to frame them in a close shot: she is seen full face, from above, and he is partially out of shot.*

NATALIE : You know very well that you are handsome, because I love you. But today you are even more handsome than usual . . . you're glowing! *He sniffs the rose, and she becomes suspicious.* What's that flower?

BAPTISTE *evasively* : Just a flower . . .

NATALIE *raising her head* : A flower! . . . It's because you're going on stage that you're so happy!

BAPTISTE : Perhaps!

> *She rests her head on* BAPTISTE'S *thigh again. Close shot of her face.*

NATALIE : I'm happy too. I've got so much faith in you . . . Oh, Baptiste, if you only wanted, we could be so happy together. *Suddenly very sad.* But you don't love me. BAPTISTE'S *hand caresses* NATALIE'S *hair.* Oh! I know, you're very fond of me!

> *Suddenly she raises her head again.*

NATALIE *aggressively* : But I'm not interested in you're being 'fond' of me. What I want is for you to love me! *A pause, then sad and tender.* It's very simple to be in love. *When he still does not say a word.* Oh! You're doing it on purpose! It's not . . . you're not in love with somebody else, are you? And that flower? Where did you get that flower? Did someone give it to you? Who gave it to you? *Gentler, imploring.* You must tell me, Baptiste; remember, you told me that I was your friend and that you'd never have any secrets from me? Tell me . . . is it a woman? Do I know her? What's her name?

> *Cut to close shot of* BAPTISTE, *full face, and* NATALIE *from the back, half out of shot, then a series of reverse angle shots favouring the one who is speaking.*

BAPTISTE : I don't know. *Speaking in a low voice, as if to himself.*

I leaned over the edge of a well. There were many of us looking at her, but I was the only one to see her.

NATALIE: Oh, Baptiste, you're still dreaming, and you're making fun of me!

BAPTISTE: No, it's the truth. What else do you want me to tell you? I saw her again today, by chance, and she gave me this flower. That's all.

NATALIE: That's all! . . . Well, it's not very much after all. *Hopefully ironic.* And, of course, you fell in love with her!

BAPTISTE *full face, close up, very serious*: Oh! . . . yes, I love her!
>*Close shot of the two of them.* NATALIE *jumps up, frightened, and steps backwards.*

NATALIE *overwhelmed*: The way you said that!
>*She stares at him, not quite knowing how to react, her eyes filling with tears. Medium long shot:* BAPTISTE *and* NATALIE *on the left, and the* STAGE MANAGER *in the background on the right. The* STAGE MANAGER *comes in and approaches them.* NATALIE *walks away from* BAPTISTE, *still staring at him, her eyes full of tears.*

STAGE MANAGER: Come on, chickens, it'll be your turn in a minute. *To* BAPTISTE. Oh! but you look splendid, Baptiste. And the flower . . . good idea, the flower, a nice touch, that'll make them laugh! Well, then . . . you know the outline. *Pointing to* NATALIE. You're in love with the little one, but she laughs in your face, so you weep like a baby. Play the love sick dunce . . . you know the sort of thing . . . you don't have to be a genius. Okay, then, off you go, kids.
>BAPTISTE, *still dreaming, gets up and goes towards the door.* NATALIE *follows him timidly.*
>[*As* NATALIE *passes by the* STAGE MANAGER *he gives her a smack on the behind. Then he notices the wedding dress that* NATALIE *had thrown aside. He stoops down, picks it up, dusts it off, looks at it, and suddenly holds it up against him and looks at himself in the mirror, laughing like an idiot.*]

(This scene was in the script, but left out when shooting because it did not fit in with the personality of NATALIE as Maria Casares had developed it, nor with the age of the STAGE MANAGER, and it would have spoiled the atmosphere of the scene.)

Outside it is night time, in front of a squalid little stall selling glasses of wine. Medium long shot of FREDERICK *and* BAPTISTE *from the back, leaning against the counter in front of a tureen of mulled wine.* FREDERICK, *the more exuberant of the two, is a bit drunk. He ladles himself great bumpers of wine, and turns towards his ' guests ', who happen to be two or three beggars he met by chance. A battered suitcase is beside him on the ground.*

FREDERICK : Exquisite, this little mulled wine ! It's like the Good Lord himself slipping down your throat, in red velvet breeches !

Reverse angle shot of the drinkers, facing the camera, so FREDERICK *is full face to the camera, and* BAPTISTE *three-quarters frontview, watching him, the full glass in his hand. He is leaning an elbow on the counter, dressed in black, a battered soft hat on his head, and the rose in his button hole.*

FREDERICK : Here's to you, Baptiste ! *They chink glasses, then* FREDERICK *turns towards the tramps.* Here's to you, friends . . . and remember that tonight you have been drinking with Julius Caesar ! Julius Caesar or somebody else . . . Charles the Bold . . . Attila . . . Henry IV . . . Ravaillac . . . *To* BAPTISTE. Yes, I'm sure of it, my destiny is to bring to life again the great men of the world. They've been lying around underground for long enough. They played their role — now it's my turn ! *He laughs.* Just let me try, and you'll see. *Pointing at one of the bemused tramps.* Julius Caesar . . . arise ! It's Frederick who calls you ! *He slaps the poor old fellow on the back.* I shall shake out his dust . . . and drag his ghost onto the stage flooded with light . . . and he will be alive again. *He bangs on the counter* . . . and he will astonish the world again because of me. *To* BAPTISTE *who is listening and smiling.* Obviously you think that's very funny !

A pause. Close shot of the two of them. FREDERICK, *facing the camera, leans an elbow on the counter to take a better look at his friend* BAPTISTE. (*Still on page 55*)

FREDERICK *shaking his head* : You don't imagine, do you, that I'm going to end my days at the ' Funambules ', in a lion's skin . . . and a lion who isn't even allowed to roar? What torture if you have, as I have, in here . . . *he taps his head* . . . and here . . . *he taps his heart* . . . a whole orchestra, a whole world !

Reverse angle shot: BAPTISTE *full face,* FREDERICK *three-*

quarters view.

FREDERICK : With you it's different. You don't need to open your mouth! BAPTISTE, *still with his glass in his hand, smiles.* Oh, I can understand that words, fine phrases, leave you cold. You don't need them, because you can say everything you want without saying anything at all! And you say it very well, you know. As a matter of fact you astonished me. *Reverse angle shot. Full face of* FREDERICK. You speak with your legs, you reply with your hands, one look, a shrug of the shoulders, two steps forward, one step backward and there you are! . . . They've understood everything, up in the Gods!

> *Close shot of* BAPTISTE *in profile.* FREDERICK *from the back, half in half out of shot.*

BAPTISTE *very serious, and still talking as if he was lost in a dream* : Yes, they understand everything. They're poor people, but I am like them. I love them, I know them well. Their lives are small, but they have big dreams. And I don't only want to make them laugh, I want to move them, to frighten them, to make them cry.

FREDERICK : And you want to do all that without saying a word!

BAPTISTE : Yes, without a word!

FREDERICK : Difficult!

BAPTISTE : You think it's impossible!

FREDERICK. No . . . difficult. It's not the same thing. *He turns towards camera to speak to the* PROPRIETOR. Well . . . let's have the bill then.

> *Medium shot — the group seen from the counter.* FREDERICK *drinks. The* PROPRIETOR *comes into shot.*

PROPRIETOR : Here it is.

FREDERICK *looking at the bill* : Think yourself lucky that I've got enough to pay you, but only just . . . only just! *As he pays he turns to* BAPTISTE. And I don't even know where I'm going to sleep tonight.

> *The* PROPRIETOR *goes out of shot. Close shot of* BAPTISTE *and* FREDERICK.

BAPTISTE : Where I do, at the ' Grand Relais '.

FREDERICK *pouring himself another ladleful of wine* : Is it a hotel?

BAPTISTE : Hardly, but they let out rooms.

FREDERICK : And give credit?

BAPTISTE : Of course, otherwise I wouldn't live there.

> FREDERICK *drinks. Wipe from above.*

61

That same night, in a room on the ground floor of a poor but clean lodging house. Medium shot of the Proprietress and Manageress, MME. HERMINE, *a woman who is no longer young, but still attractive. She is standing in front of a chest of drawers, from which she picks up an oil lamp.*

MME. HERMINE *with a charming smile*: Really, are you sure you wouldn't prefer the little suite on the first floor?

Reverse angle shot of BAPTISTE *and* FREDERICK *on the doorstep.*

FREDERICK: No, I assure you . . . one little room is enough for me.

MME. HERMINE *comes towards them with the lamp in her hand, and takes down a key from a numbered board on the wall.*

MME. HERMINE: Pity! *Dreamily, gazing tenderly at* FREDERICK. It would make such an attractive apartment for a young man . . . a pair of flowered curtains . . . Oh, well, I'll show you the rooms at the top of the house first, and you can choose.

FREDERICK: I'm sorry to disturb you so late . . . Madame . . .

Slight note of interrogation in his voice.

MME. HERMINE: Madame Hermine. But don't apologise, I'm used to going to sleep late. And even then . . . sometimes I read for hours when I am in bed.

FREDERICK *gallantly*: . . . love stories, I'm sure!

MME. HERMINE *to* BAPTISTE, *with a little laugh*: Oh! really, Monsieur Baptiste, I think you've brought along a young man who knows all about women, and their little weaknesses. *She opens the door.* Go ahead, please . . . *discreetly curious* . . . Monsieur?

FREDERICK *always trying to charm*: Frederick . . . Frederick Lemaître. *He picks up his suitcase, and makes a little bow in front of the door.* After you . . . I promise that I won't make anything of it, Madame Hermine.

MM. HERMINE *coy*: Oh! . . . Oh! . . . thank you, Monsieur Frederick!

The camera tracks backwards in front of MME. HERMINE *carrying the lamp and the two men as they cross the court-yard. When they reach the outside staircase that leads to the upper floors,* BAPTISTE *stops, and the two others do the same.*

BAPTISTE: Well, then, good night Frederick . . . and good night

Madame Hermine.

He leaves them, and goes out of the building.

FREDERICK *surprised*: Where's he off to at this hour of night?

MME. HERMINE: Oh, he always goes off. *Sighs.* He's out every night.

FREDERICK *admiringly*: Well, well, good for him! A real alley cat, Monsieur Baptiste!

Medium shot, slightly high angle, of the two of them, who have already climbed several steps. FREDERICK, *very theatrical, gestures towards the shadows, out of shot, which have just swallowed up* BAPTISTE.

FREDERICK *declaiming*:

' Silent and furtive like a cat in the night,
    He flits to the shadows where his love awaits him,
    He goes to the one he loves, his beauty, his pleasure,
    His mistress, alone and naked, trembling with desire.'

MME. HERMINE *excited and embarrassed*: Beautiful . . . yes . . . yes . . . but it's a bit . . . a bit . . .

FREDERICK *gently suggestive*: A bit . . .?

MME. HERMINE *blushing*: Oh! I beg you, Monsieur Frederick . . . you'll make me say something silly. Go ahead, please. *She giggles.*

FREDERICK *very gallantly*: After you . . .

MME. HERMINE *bows her head, and passes in front of* FREDERICK.

Shot of a long corridor on the first floor. There are doors opening off it on both sides. MME. HERMINE, *still followed by* FREDERICK *appears at the end of the corridor.*

MME. HERMINE: Here are the rooms. *She opens a door on the right.* This one isn't bad at all.

FREDERICK *looking in*: Oh, that's charming, that's very nice.

MME. HERMINE *opens another door, leaving the key in the door of the previous room. (Important that this should be noticed — marked in the original script.)*

MME. HERMINE: Or if you would prefer that one, with the double bed.

FREDERICK *still gently suggestive*: Oh, yes, I definitely prefer a double bed.

They go into the room.

The camera pans round the room. It is furnished very simply, but cleanly. A large bed, a window, a fireplace, and a table in the middle. FREDERICK *puts down his suitcase on the bed.*

FREDERICK: Ah, poor Frederick! . . . Lost, all night . . . lost, in a big bed! Ah! . . . beds are made to sleep in, don't you think so, Madame Hermine?

MME. HERMINE: Of course, Monsieur Frederick!

As she speaks, MME. HERMINE *has moved to light the lamp on the table. Then, the camera pans to follow her as she returns to* FREDERICK.

MME. HERMINE *regretfully*: Well, then . . . I'll leave you. Good night. The key is in the door . . .

She goes towards the door. The camera pans towards FREDERICK, *his suitcase open in front of him, and some books in his hand. He goes towards the mantelpiece.*

FREDERICK *shrugging his shoulders*: Oh! I don't bother with the key. I always leave my door open . . .

MME. HERMINE: Really?

FREDERICK *smiling*: Yes; one never knows, after all . . . a pretty woman could be passing, and mistake the room for hers! . . .

MME. HERMINE *sighing sadly*: A pretty woman! . . . Young people nowadays are difficult to please . . .

Close shot of the two of them. FREDERICK *takes her by the shoulders.*

FREDERICK: Did I say that you were ugly, Mme. Hermine?

He takes the lamp out of her hand. (Still on page 55)

MME. HERMINE *overwhelmed and stammering*: Oh! . . . Oh! . . . Monsieur Frederick! . . . oh! Monsieur Frederick! . . .

Fade out.

Outside, it is still night-time at Ménilmontant, by the town wall. A desolate, empty part of the world. To the right there is a high wall. In the background the town boundary itself, and rooftops. The camera tracks forward and stops finally on a close shot of a BLIND BEGGAR *sitting on the pavement. Beside him is an empty bird cage, and on his shoulder a starved looking owl.*

BLIND BEGGAR *chanting*: Have pity on a poor blind man . . .

He repeats it several times, shaking a tin bowl with a few sous in it. Cut back to the previous shot, looking down the street. In the distance someone is approaching. It is BAPTISTE. *As he reaches the* BLIND BEGGAR, *he suddenly starts to walk on tiptoe.*

BLIND BEGGAR *raising his voice into a pitiful wail*: Have pity on a poor blind man . . . don't go away . . . I can hear your footsteps very well . . . *Close shot of the* BEGGAR. Why are you walking on tiptoe? . . . Why?

Medium shot of the BLIND BEGGAR *in the foreground, three-quarters back view;* BAPTISTE *stops, astonished.*

BLIND BEGGAR: To avoid me? So that you don't have to give me anything? So that you don't have to give alms to a poor, poor blind man? . . . Why?

Low angle shot of BAPTISTE *as he comes closer.*

BAPTISTE *very simply*: Because I haven't got any money.

Series of reverse angle shots, according to who is speaking. The BLIND BEGGAR *from above, as seen by* BAPTISTE *from below as ' seen ' by the* BLIND BEGGAR.

BLIND BEGGAR *surprised*: No money! . . . *He turns to his bird.* Do you hear that, bird? Really, it makes you laugh. There are so many people walking about with well-lined pockets. It's so simple to take it, money from pockets . . . when one can see!

BAPTISTE *smiling*: Perhaps, but that's not my trade.

BLIND BEGGAR *off — the camera is still on* BAPTISTE: His trade! *He laughs.* Do you hear that, bird? He hasn't got a penny, but he's got a trade! . . . *Shot of the* BEGGAR. That's a fine trade, that feeds the ones who practise it so well!

Medium shot of the two of them.

BAPTISTE: All the same, it is a fine trade! Do you mind if I keep you company for a bit? I've been walking for a long time, and I'm rather tired.

He sits down on the pavement next to the BLIND BEGGAR.
Medium shot of the two of them. (Still on page 56)

BLIND BEGGAR: All the same, I'd be interested to know why you're wandering about like this, in the middle of the night?

BAPTISTE *full face, the* BLIND BEGGAR *half out of shot.*

BAPTISTE: To see!

BLIND BEGGAR *off — the camera still on* BAPTISTE: To see! Do you hear that . . . bird?

The BEGGAR *three-quarters front view,* BAPTISTE *half-out of shot.*

65

BLIND BEGGAR *shrugging his shoulders* : To see what, I'd like to know!

BAPTISTE *reverse angle shot* : Everything!

BLIND BEGGAR *reverse angle shot — suspicious* : Oh . . . wait a minute. You're too eager, you are. Too curious by half. *His tone changes.* Here, you . . . wandering around all night . . . your trade, it wouldn't be . . . *He imitates the buzzing of a bee.* Bzz . . . bzz . . . would it?

BAPTISTE *smiling* : No, don't worry, that isn't what I do.

BLIND BEGGAR : Oh, it's not that we're worried, but informers — we don't like them, the bird and I! So, what do you do then? Are you going to tell us?

BAPTISTE *very simply* : I work at the ' Theatre des Funambules '.

BLIND BEGGAR *half out of shot* : At the theatre? Do you sell oranges?

BAPTISTE : No, I act.

BLIND BEGGAR : You act?

BAPTISTE : Yes . . . I mime.

BLIND BEGGAR *suddenly enthusiastic* : Oh! The pantomime . . . I love the pantomime . . . I go there all the time!

Series of cross cuts, but full face this time.

BAPTISTE *amazed* : What! You . . . ?

BLIND BEGGAR *a bit embarrassed* : Oh, of course, I can't see anything, but I take a friend, and he tells me what is happening. That's how I know what's going on. *More and more pleased to have met* BAPTISTE. Well then, you're an actor! . . . but you should have said so right away. We'll have to celebrate that. Yes, we'll go and have a drink.

The BLIND BEGGAR *gets up. The camera tracks backwards to frame both of them in a close shot.*

BLIND BEGGAR : And when I say a drink!

BAPTISTE *getting up* : You're very kind . . . thank you.

BLIND BEGGAR : Thank me when we're drunk . . . *He bends down; picks up the cage, and puts the owl inside.* In with you, bird, . . . off we go, the carriage is ordered. *To* BAPTISTE. Anyway, we're not going far. Just next door, to the ' Robin Redbreast '. *He laughs.* You, who like to learn things, this'll amuse you!

BAPTISTE : Do you want me to help you?

BLIND BEGGAR : No thanks, I know the way.

They walk along slowly. Cheap music, slightly muffled. The
camera tracks sideways to reveal in the shadows the rather
sinister façade of 'The Robin Redbreast'.

BLIND BEGGAR: Pretty name, isn't it, 'The Robin Redbreast'?
It's called that after one of the men who used to own it. One night,
someone slit his throat . . . *with a suitable gesture* . . . right there,
behind his own bar. So, you understand why 'The Robin Redbreast' seemed the obvious name, after that.

General shot of the interior of 'The Robin Redbreast'. *It is*
a dance hall with the doorway seen right at the back; the
dance floor on the left, and above it a balcony for the
musicians. Around the dance floor are wooden tables and
benches. The place itself is not particularly sordid, but the
clientele — pale, shifty-eyed crooks, tramps and old hags, and
youngsters in dubious finery give it its particular atmosphere
of rather sinister squalor.

Old women, plastered with make-up, ruined by years of pros-
titution, are collapsed in heaps in front of their glasses. Pretty
girls, still juicy and happy to be alive burst out laughing from
time to time. The music and the general noise of the place
can be heard. Some people are playing cards, and others
sleeping with their heads on the table. The orchestra, on their
balcony, are playing a popular tune, and on the dance floor,
two or three couples are dancing, bumping into a drunkard
whenever he gets in their way. He is conscientiously trying to
dance balancing on one leg, although he cannot even stand up
straight any longer; he falls down, gets up and tries over and
over again, obsessively. Two WAITERS *come and go, watched*
over by the PROPRIETOR, *a giant with anxious, furtive eyes, who*
stands behind his bar inspecting this fine collection of people.

Slightly high angle long shot, then the BLIND BEGGAR *comes*
into the café followed by BAPTISTE, *and the camera tracks*
sideways to follow them, panning first in one direction then in
the other. The BLIND BEGGAR *salutes the* PROPRIETOR *with his*
hand and goes towards a table in the background. The camera
tracks sideways to follow them through the crowd to the table.

BLIND BEGGAR: Sit down. Here, we can be comfortable. This is my
beat.

They sit down, facing each other. The BLIND BEGGAR *puts the bird cage on the table. A* WAITER *comes up. Close shot of the group.*

WAITER : Evening, Fil de Soie.

FIL DE SOIE : Evening, little Louis. Wine for two, and something nice to eat. I've got a guest.

WAITER : And something for the bird?

FIL DE SOIE *shrugging his shoulders* : Of course !

The WAITER *moves off. The camera follows him: it pans to reveal a young man in a greasy cap: he is coming towards their table. Pan back in the opposite direction, with the young man. Shot of the three of them; the young man remains standing, leaning down towards* FIL DE SOIE.

Close shot of the three of them. BAPTISTE *and* FIL DE SOIE *from the side, and the* YOUNG MAN *between them, facing the camera. He takes two rings out of his handkerchief and throws them on the table, to* BAPTISTE'S *astonishment.*

YOUNG MAN : Is this junk, or the real thing?

FIL DE SOIE : Wait a minute and I'll tell you.

Close shot of FIL DE SOIE *from the front and* BAPTISTE *half out of the picture.* FIL DE SOIE *takes a jeweller's glass out of his pocket and carefully examines the jewels. Reverse angle shot of the astounded face of* BAPTISTE. *Cut back to close shot of the three of them.*

FIL DE SOIE *giving back the rings* : It's the real thing. You haven't been robbed !

YOUNG MAN *putting them back in his handkerchief* : Good ! Thanks.

Close shot of BAPTISTE, *still stupefied with astonishment, then shot of both of them,* BAPTISTE *three-quarters back view. The* WAITER *brings two glasses and a bottle.*

FIL DE SOIE : You can't believe your eyes, can you, actor? *Smiling.* But it's really very simple. Outside I'm blind . . . incurable, I'm afraid . . . *He pours out the drinks* . . . not a glimmer of light . . . and in here I'm cured. . . It's a miracle, isn't it? So I do a few odd jobs : value things, jewellery, precious stones, gold . . . things like that. *Giving* BAPTISTE *a friendly tap on the shoulder.* What do you think of that, actor?

Reverse angle shot of the two of them. BAPTISTE *looks at his companion, smiling slightly, almost admiringly, but without*

saying anything. Cut back to the previous shot, with FIL DE
SOIE *facing the camera.*

FIL DE SOIE : You don't say anything . . . you're a wise man!
That's the best way, never say anything.

*The music ends. Long shot, slightly high angle, of the room;
general applause.*

*Medium shot of the door of the tavern which opens to let in
the* OLD CLOTHES MAN. *He is not carrying his bundle of old
clothes any more, but simply a small bag filled with almanacs,
one of which he is brandishing in the air as he cries in a
harsh, strident, drunken voice.*

OLD CLOTHES MAN *shouting*: Have you been dreaming of cats?
Have you been dreaming of dogs? Have you been dreaming of
troubled waters? *Waving the almanac.* Here is the explanation of
all your dreams : a real book, with illustrations ! . . .

*The camera tracks sideways and pans to follow him to the
bar on the left. Medium shot of the* PROPRIETOR, *three-
quarters back view, in the foreground. The* OLD CLOTHES
MAN *comes up to him. The table of* BAPTISTE *and* FIL DE SOIE
is somewhere in the background.

OLD CLOTHES MAN : Evening, patron ! . . . *in an undertone . . .*
Lacenaire isn't far away, but I haven't said anything. Understood?

PATRON : Understood. Thanks.

[*The camera pans rapidly down to the drawer underneath
the bar. The* PATRON'S *hand opens it. Inside can be seen two
pistols. The hand shuts the drawer, and the camera pans
quickly up to the two men again. The* OLD CLOTHES MAN
makes a sign to the PATRON *that he has understood, then goes
off towards the table of* BAPTISTE *and* FIL DE SOIE.]

(This little scene was shot and edited, but cut from most
versions shown.)

*The Orchestra starts playing again while the camera is track-
ing sideways through the crowd of drinkers to follow the* OLD
CLOTHES MAN.

OLD CLOTHES MAN : Here I am, Jericho, called the Trumpet,
known as the Sandman, or Sweet Sleep, because I can cure bad
dreams. Have you been dreaming of snakes, fires, newborn babes?

Close shot of FIL DE SOIE *and* BAPTISTE *at their table. The*
OLD CLOTHES MAN *stops by* FIL DE SOIE *and takes out of*

his pocket a gold watch and shows it to FIL DE SOIE.

OLD CLOTHES MAN *smiling with satisfaction* : It doesn't look like much, Fil de Soie, but it's a real collectors' piece! *Recognising* BAPTISTE, *he immediately puts the watch in his pocket.* Well, for goodness sake! . . . what on earth are you doing here, Baptiste? This isn't your sort of place. You should be ashamed of yourself, hanging around a dump like this! If Debureau could see you . . . and what about Natalie? What would she think?

Close shot, slightly high angle, of BAPTISTE *from the point of view of the* OLD CLOTHES MAN.

BAPTISTE *aggressively* : I forbid you to mention Natalie's name.

Reverse angle shot: the OLD CLOTHES MAN *as seen by* BAPTISTE, *slightly low angle.*

OLD CLOTHES MAN *hypocritically sweet* : All the same, a sweet young girl like that . . . fresh as a rose, pure as a lily.

BAPTISTE *cut back to him, his teeth clenched* : Be quiet! I don't want to listen to you. I don't like you. I can't stand you . . . you know it very well, I've already told you. Leave me alone . . .

Close shot of the three of them : FIL DE SOIE, *without any signs of noticing what is going on, gives food to his bird. The* OLD CLOTHES MAN *turns towards him.*

OLD CLOTHES MAN: Do you hear that, Fil de Soie . . . *shrugging his shoulders.* You try to do someone a favour! *To* BAPTISTE. What I said was for your own good. *He turns round towards the door.* Look, here comes some high society!

Medium shot of the door: LACENAIRE *makes a grand entrance. On his right arm is* GARANCE, *and on his left,* AVRIL. LACENAIRE *is still wearing the same clothes, but he has added a cane with which he plays negligently. Two other characters, dressed in style, but a bit vulgar and crumpled at the same time, accompany the trio.* LACENAIRE *looks round the room.*

PATRON *lowering his eyes* : Evening, Monsieur Lacenaire.

LACENAIRE *replies with a reassuring gesture. Cut back to a close shot of the table where* BAPTISTE *and* FIL DE SOIE *are sitting.* BAPTISTE *turns round and recognises* GARANCE. *Suddenly his face lights up. (Still on page 56)*

BAPTISTE *under his breath* : Oh! . . . Oh! . . . It's marvellous.

FIL DE SOIE : What's marvellous?

BAPTISTE *radiant* : Life . . . everything!

His eyes follow them and the camera tracks backwards and pans to keep the group in medium shot. LACENAIRE *and his group, passing through a wave of flattering murmurs, and general esteem, crosses the dance floor and makes for a table at the back.*

The camera tracks backwards, in front of them. LACENAIRE, *very relaxed, continues a story he is telling.*

LACENAIRE : His lawyer had told him ' most important, never confess. Say nothing.' But the chaplain had said, ' a sin confessed is half forgiven ', so he confessed !

Close shot of BAPTISTE, *full face, following them with his eyes . . . and cut back to pan with the group in medium shot, as they come to a table. As he is speaking,* LACENAIRE *pulls out a chair for* GARANCE, *and then sits on her right.*

LACENAIRE : ' Perfect,' said the judge. ' You have killed, you have confessed . . . perfect, perfect, your head will be cut off.'

The others roar with laughter.

GARANCE *alone stays silent, bored, unmoved. The three dubious characters sit down.* AVRIL *takes a chair facing* LACENAIRE. *Close shot of the group, slightly high angle. A* WAITER *comes up and puts some glasses and a bottle on the table.*

LACENAIRE *continuing* : So, the other poor chap, you understand he was a bit disappointed. He protested; ' Hey, wait a minute ! They told me ' a sin confessed is . . .' ' Is half forgiven ', replied the judge. ' That's right, perfectly true . . . but as justice must be done, all the same, we'll just have half your head cut off ! '

Louder laughter.

FIRST FRIEND OF LACENAIRE : Oh ! That's a good one !

SECOND FRIEND OF LACENAIRE : He's terrific this Lacenaire, he can always make you laugh.

Close shot of BAPTISTE. *He never stops staring at* GARANCE. *Close shot of her.*

AVRIL *off* : He talks just like a book, doesn't he ?

Medium shot of BAPTISTE, *the* OLD CLOTHES MAN *and* FIL DE SOIE. *The* OLD CLOTHES MAN *leaves them, his head lowered.* BAPTISTE *does not even notice.*

Cut back to a close shot of GARANCE *and* LACENAIRE. *The latter finishes pouring out the wine, and puts the bottle, now empty, down on the table.* LACENAIRE, *looking at* GARANCE, *who is still silent and distant, puts his arm round her.*

LACENAIRE : Why are you so quiet? So sad, my sweet angel? Come on, life is beautiful!

GARANCE *very cold and aggressive* : If you find life so beautiful, Pierre-François, why are you always talking about death?

LACENAIRE *smiling* : Don't worry, Garance, I always talk about the death of others. My own is for later . . . And then . . . that's what life is! . . . *He drinks.* Philosophers are always thinking of death, and beautiful women of love . . . *to the others* . . . Isn't that true?

> GARANCE *looks at them all, and then points at each in turn, amused.*

GARANCE : So, if I understand you correctly, insofar as you are all sitting here, you are all philosophers!

LACENAIRE : Why not?

GARANCE *bursting out laughing* : Well, I must say, philosophy is gay, pretty, clean!

> *Close shot of* BAPTISTE, *full face, still looking at* GARANCE. *He is full of admiration, overcome and dazed. Cut back to* LACENAIRE *and* GARANCE.

LACENAIRE *lowering his voice, hurt* : And love, that's always gay and beautiful . . . I suppose?

GARANCE *with a calm smile, very sure of what she says* : It's certainly better.

> *The music stops at the end of the second dance. Close shot of* FIL DE SOIE *and* BAPTISTE.

FIL DE SOIE *looking at* BAPTISTE : For goodness sakes, I've seen people fall for a girl, but never like that! . . . Well, I've no advice to give you, but if you want to wake up tomorrow morning alive, it wouldn't be a bad idea to go home to bed right now. It's that little lot who fixed the man who used to be Patron here. Of course, I shouldn't tell you, but . . .

> BAPTISTE *obviously has not heard a word. He is still looking at* GARANCE, *and smiling.*

BAPTISTE : She doesn't love him. It's obvious . . . She doesn't love him.

> *General shot of the dance floor. Medium shot of* LACENAIRE'S *table as seen by* BAPTISTE. *Suddenly,* GARANCE *gets up and takes a step in the direction of the dance floor.* LACENAIRE *gets*

up to join her, and takes her arm. Close shot of the two of them, face to face.

LACENAIRE : Do you really want to go, Garance?

GARANCE : Yes ... I'm tired, and I'm bored.

LACENAIRE *suddenly feverish, losing his usual self-control* : Listen, Garance, this is serious. This is something I've never felt for any woman ...

GARANCE *interrupting him, gently ironic* : Love, Pierre-François, love!

LACENAIRE *brutal* : That's got nothing to do with it! *Lowering his voice.* I want you, Garance, that's all. But I've got my pride.

GARANCE *interrupting him again* : ... and you would like ... to love ... *Lowering her eyes, modest and ironic, but very firm.* Your head is too hot for me, Pierre-François, and your heart too cold. I'm afraid of draughts. I don't want to lose my health ... my gaiety ...

LACENAIRE *shrugging his shoulders* : It's a pity. We could have done remarkable things together. *Making an effort to laugh again.* I would have caused oceans of blood to flow for you! ... and rivers of diamonds! ...

> *As he says these words, the camera follows him as he goes back to the table and sits down. Shot of* GARANCE, *slightly low angle, as seen by* LACENAIRE, *standing next to the table.*

GARANCE *still smiling* : I don't ask for all that!

> *The* OLD CLOTHES MAN *comes into shot and takes* GARANCE'S *hand.*

OLD CLOTHES MAN : Oh, what beautiful hands! *Towards* LACENAIRE, *who is out of shot.* May I, Lacenaire? *Close-up of* OLD CLOTHES MAN *and* GARANCE. Shall I read your future, my beauty? GARANCE *shrugging her shoulders:* If you want to! But I warn you, I don't believe in it. *Looking towards* LACENAIRE, *out of shot.* I only believe in what I love.

LACENAIRE *off* : For instance?

GARANCE *coming back to sit beside* LACENAIRE; *the camera pans to take in her and* LACENAIRE *sitting, and the* OLD CLOTHES MAN *standing* : Oh, nothing particular, no one in particular. *To the* OLD CLOTHES MAN. Still, it would give me pleasure if you saw a journey.

OLD CLOTHES MAN *looking at her hand* : Ah, yes, and I do see a journey! . . . in fact a very long journey. (*Still on page 73*)

GARANCE : To India, perhaps?

LACENAIRE : Why India, Garance?

GARANCE : Because it's far away!

LACENAIRE : That's enough, Jericho, the consultation is over.

The OLD CLOTHES MAN *obeys and is going off . . . when* LACENAIRE *stops him with a gesture. Close-up of* LACENAIRE, *slightly high angle, beside* GARANCE. *The* OLD CLOTHES MAN *already almost out of shot, has turned round.*

LACENAIRE : Tell me, since you also know how to interpret dreams . . . *He points to the almanac . . .* interpret this one for me. Last night, I dreamed of you.

Close-up of OLD CLOTHES MAN *from the front, low angle,* LACENAIRE *and* AVRIL *from the back half out of shot.*

LACENAIRE : Yes. You were going along the road crying your wares : ' Old Clothes Man, have you any clothes to sell? ' . . . *High angle shot of* LACENAIRE . . . and, in my dream, I heard something else. Yes, I heard you cry, ' seller of old friends, have you any friends to sell? ' *Abruptly.* Is it true, what I hear? That you have your little ways of getting in touch with ' them ' and that you shop your friends, Jericho?

Camera pans slowly round all the sinister, watching faces at the table. Series of reverse angle shots, high angle and low angle, according to whom is speaking.

OLD CLOTHES MAN *frightened and caught out* : It's a lie, . . . I swear, as my name is . . .

LACENAIRE : As your name is turncoat, twister, Judas, informer . . .

OLD CLOTHES MAN *insulted* : Oh! How can people be so wicked!

LACENAIRE *smiling more and more* : I have no evil intentions but I would be happier to know that you were discreet, Jericho.

The OLD CLOTHES MAN *sheepishly goes out of shot. Cut back to high angle close shot of* LACENAIRE *and* GARANCE.

LACENAIRE *lowering his voice, to* GARANCE : It is you who will betray me, my angel. That is your right.

Cut to the orchestra which is just beginning a new dance, and cut back to the two of them in close shot still sitting down, facing the camera.

GARANCE : No, Pierre-François, you're making a mistake.

LACENAIRE : Yes, my angel, you will betray me . . . and if I have to, I'll help you to do it.

He tries to take her hand, but she pulls away and stands up.

GARANCE : Leave me alone . . . you wear me down, I came here to have fun, to dance . . .

BAPTISTE *off* : Will you dance with me?

She turns round, suddenly. Medium shot of BAPTISTE *standing beside her, smiling and ignoring the others. Close-up of her, as she smiles back. Close-up of* LACENAIRE *showing no emotion. Close-up of* BAPTISTE, *smiling. Close-up of* AVRIL *dumbfounded. Medium shot of* GARANCE *and* BAPTISTE *face to face, the others half out of shot. Astonished and overwhelmed* GARANCE *stares at* BAPTISTE, *and holds out her hand. The camera follows them as they go onto the dance floor. Medium long shot, slightly high angle as they dance among the crowd of couples. Close-up of the table.*

AVRIL *facing camera* : Well! Monsieur Lacenaire!

LACENAIRE, *facing the camera, says nothing, but smiles oddly. Medium shot of the orchestra playing, and slow pan downwards to frame in a slightly high angle shot of the dance floor, where* GARANCE *and* BAPTISTE *dance as if they were alone in the world.* (N.B. Carné had imagined a shot where they were dancing alone, in a dream, but he did not shoot it.) *Cut back to the table, where the* OLD CLOTHES MAN *has reappeared, and is standing by* LACENAIRE'S *shoulder, leaning down to him.*

AVRIL : But I mean to say . . . Monsieur Lacenaire! . . .

LACENAIRE *without listening* : Who is it?

OLD CLOTHES MAN : He's nobody. A little actor from the ' Theatre des Funambules.'

LACENAIRE *with contempt* : An actor! What creatures! *Nodding his head.* The Church was right when it used to bury those people in the dead of night.

Medium close-up of the couple dancing.

GARANCE *happy and smiling* : It's funny, I didn't recognise you at first! But you know, you'd better be careful. They can be very nasty . . . I'm warning you.

BAPTISTE : It doesn't matter. What can they do to me? I'm so happy.

GARANCE looks at him surprised.

79

Close-up of FIL DE SOIE, *sitting at his table, and watching the couple dance. The camera follows his gaze which shifts to* LACENAIRE'S *table.* AVRIL *winks and makes a gesture towards the dance floor. The* OLD CLOTHES MAN *is no longer there.*

AVRIL : Well, Monsieur Lacenaire?

LACENAIRE *very casual* : All right, Avril, if it would amuse you.

AVRIL *gets up, puts the flower he has been holding behind his ear, and with the camera tracking backwards in front of him, he walks towards the dance floor* . . . *singing his favourite tune as he goes* . . .

[AVRIL *singing his favourite tune* :
       Love is a sweet child found
       Love is a sweet child lost . . .]

(Actually he does not sing the words in the film, but whistles.)
       [*Close-up of* FIL DE SOIE *at his table, knowing what is going to happen.*

FIL DE SOIE *to his owl* : What can one do, bird? . . . I told you, didn't I?] (Cut in final version.)

The camera tracks backwards, then pans, to follow AVRIL, *from behind, approaching* GARANCE *and* BAPTISTE. *The people move aside.* AVRIL *taps* BAPTISTE *on the shoulder;* BAPTISTE, *surprised, turns round.*

BAPTISTE : Yes?

Without replying, AVRIL *seizes* BAPTISTE *by the collar.* GARANCE, *horrified and angry, takes hold of* AVRIL *by the arm.* (*Still on page 73*)

GARANCE : Leave him alone!

Still without a word AVRIL *turns his head towards* . . . *Medium shot of a large window. Cut back to a close-up of the three of them. Still holding* BAPTISTE *by the collar of his jacket,* AVRIL *pushes him towards the window with extraordinary rapidity, the camera panning to follow. Close-up of* GARANCE *facing the camera, she turns her head away. Medium shot of the window, shot slightly from below;* BAPTISTE, *still propelled by* AVRIL, *comes into shot moving backwards and to the left. Then* AVRIL, *pushing him in the face with unbelievable brutality, sends him smashing violently into the window, which breaks.* BAPTISTE *tumbles backwards and disappears in a shower of broken glass.*

Long shot of the room: everyone is laughing. Close-up of the orchestra, the musicians are splitting their sides, without pausing in their music. In medium shot, the camera tracks backwards to reveal the PATRON *behind his bar; he rushes up to* AVRIL.

PATRON : And what about my window?

LACENAIRE *off* : Come on, patron!

The PATRON, *frightened, and* AVRIL, *very cold, turn towards* LACENAIRE.

Medium shot, shot very slightly from above, of LACENAIRE, *sitting at his table.*

LACENAIRE : Can't people enjoy themselves any longer at the 'Robin Redbreast?' *He touches his throat.*

Laughter. Cut back to AVRIL *and the* PATRON. *The latter blenches.*

PATRON *stammering* : Yes, yes, of course, Monsieur La-Lacenaire . . . *trying to make a joke of it* . . . I don't know what I was talking about!

AVRIL *passes in front of him to get back to his place, obviously very satisfied with himself. Medium shot of* GARANCE *going towards the door, and cut back to the crowd. Suddenly, the laughter gets louder. Surprised,* AVRIL *turns back to the centre of the dance floor, and cannot believe his eyes.*

Medium shot of the door. BAPTISTE *has just stepped in again. He is dusting himself off, very calm, smiling. Then, still equally calm, he walks, the camera panning and tracking with him, back to the broken window, and looks for something on the floor. He sees it, bends down, and picks up the rose* GARANCE *had given him, which he had lost in the fight. He sticks it into his lapel again, looking at* GARANCE. *Close-up of* GARANCE, *then close-up of* AVRIL.

[AVRIL : Very good. Okay. We'll have a bit of a laugh.] (Not heard in the version shown.)

He advances without hurrying, very tough, rolling his shoulders. Close-up of BAPTISTE, *who looks at* AVRIL *and smiles. A pause, then suddenly, doing a quick turn he gives* AVRIL *a great kick in the stomach.* AVRIL *takes the full force of the blow and sits down hard on the floor. Howls of laughter.*

AVRIL : Aygh! . . .

He collapses.
Close-up of FIL DE SOIE.

FIL DE SOIE : Well bird, what do you have to say about that!

Close-up, then tracking backwards, medium long shot of BAPTISTE, *innocent and smiling, as he goes up to* GARANCE *who is dumbfounded.*

BAPTISTE : It's late. Shall I take you home?

GARANCE *smiles, and lets him take her arm. They walk towards the door and go out. Music. Long shot of the crowd, as they start dancing again. In the crowd,* AVRIL *staggers to his feet, and holds his back, groaning with pain. Close-up of* LACENAIRE, *sitting at his table facing the camera; he has been watching the scene with surprise . . . anger . . . rage. Close-up of the table.* AVRIL *comes into shot, sits down, rubbing first his stomach then his back, and pouring himself a drink, he drinks it under the contemptuous gaze of* LACENAIRE. *Slightly to one side the* OLD CLOTHES MAN *follows the scene with his eyes.*

AVRIL *pathetic* : All the same, Monsieur Lacenaire!

LACENAIRE *smiling contemptuously* : My poor Avril . . .

A friend of LACENAIRE'S *points towards the couple as they go.*

FRIEND OF LACENAIRE : Well? What are we going to do?

LACENAIRE : Nothing! . . . And if there's one of you who thinks it necessary to say anything else . . . I am not one of those who are prepared to complicate their lives for the sake of a woman . . . Women! They barely exist. Let's talk about something serious.

He turns meaningfully towards the OLD CLOTHES MAN — *the latter understands, and goes off. The camera pans with him as he disappears among the dancers, it then returns to the table.* LACENAIRE, *facing the camera is in the middle.* AVRIL *is on one side half out of shot, and the others backview, half out of shot.*

LACENAIRE : This time, we have to do something worth while.

AVRIL *furious* : If it means knocking someone off, I'm for it!

LACENAIRE *ironic* : Thank you, Avril . . . *As he continues, the camera tracks slowly in towards him.* At the end of every month the debt collectors walk around the streets carrying small fortunes. It's very tempting! But to attack one outside would be commonplace and dangerous. And then there's the risk of catching cold. It's much better to work at home . . . have the client come by appointment.

AVRIL *off, low voice, admiringly*: Oh! . . . Monsieur Lacenaire!

LACENAIRE *continuing*: So I hire an apartment, I draw up a false draft, and when the cashier turns up . . .

AVRIL *off, vulgar laugh*: He cashes in his chips!

LACENAIRE: You understand everything, Avril . . . one can't hide anything from you!

> *Fade out.*
>
> *Outside it is night. The wall of Ménilmontant — empty and deserted in the darkness. A couple are walking slowly along in the background, following the wall where the* BLIND BEGGAR *had been sitting earlier on. Long shot, then medium shot, with the camera tracking sideways and backwards in front of them.*

GARANCE *looking at* BAPTISTE *and smiling*: All the same, looking at you, one would never think you were so strong.

BAPTISTE: I'm not strong.

GARANCE: But — just now you knocked down that great bully!

BAPTISTE: I had a tough childhood. I had to learn to defend myself.

> GARANCE *stops to reply to* BAPTISTE, *and so does the camera.*

GARANCE: You were unhappy.

BAPTISTE *medium close-up, full face*: When I was unhappy I slept. I dreamed . . . but people don't like it if you dream. *Smiling.* So they knock you about, as they say ' to wake you up a bit '. *Eyes bright, teeth clenched.* Luckily my sleep was tough, tougher than their blows, and I escaped them by dreaming. I dreamed . . . I hope . . . I waited . . .

> *He turns towards* GARANCE. *Pan to a shot of both of them from the front. He takes her hand.*

BAPTISTE: Perhaps it was for you that I was waiting.

> GARANCE *pulls away her hand gently and goes over to lean against the wall on the right, the camera panning to follow her.*

GARANCE *ironic*: Already!

> BAPTISTE *has followed her. He is on her right, leaning only his hand on the wall. Close-up of* BAPTISTE *three-quarters view and* GARANCE *in profile half out of shot. Then a series of reverse shots favouring the one who is speaking.*

BAPTISTE *very serious* : Why not? Perhaps I saw you in my dreams
. . . don't smile at me. Today, when you threw me that flower,
perhaps you woke me up for ever!

GARANCE *surprised and touched* : What a strange boy you are!

BAPTISTE *gazing at her, enraptured* : How beautiful you are!

GARANCE *shrugging her shoulders* : I'm not beautiful. I'm alive,
that's all.

BAPTISTE *leaning his face close to hers, his voice trembling with
emotion* : You are the most alive of all. I will never forget tonight,
and the light of your eyes.

GARANCE : Oh, the light of my eyes! *She smiles.* Just a little flicker
like everyone else! *She takes him by the arm and makes a gesture
of the head to indicate something in the distance.* Look at all
those little points of light. The lights of Ménilmontant. *Cut to a
long shot of Ménilmontant by night, with a few windows still
alight; she continues off.* People go to sleep, and wake up. Each
one has a lamp that lights up and is put out. *Cut back to her in
close-up, full face, he is backview, half out of shot.* When I think
. . . *Very melancholy* . . . that I can't even recognise the room
where I lived with my mother when I was little.

    *Series of reverse shots in medium close-up, favouring the one
    who is speaking.*

BAPTISTE : You used to live in Ménilmontant?

GARANCE : I was born here, and I lived here happily for a long
time. Very happily, . . . and yet my mother was poor, and my
father had left her. She worked in other people's houses, as a
laundress. *Quick cut to him, and medium shot of them both. She
takes a few steps; he follows her.* She loved me and I loved her. She
was beautiful, she was gay, . . . she taught me to laugh, and to sing.
. . . *Abruptly* . . . Then she died, and everything changed.

BAPTISTE *camera on him* : So you were all alone?

GARANCE *camera on her* : At fifteen! *She gestures towards Ménilmontant.* Round here a girl who has grown up too fast doesn't stay
alone very long.

    Medium close-up of them both : BAPTISTE *turns to face
    *GARANCE, *resting his right arm against the wall.*

BAPTISTE *moved* : I beg you, don't be sad. It wrings my heart.

GARANCE : Sad, me? But I'm as gay as a lark. *She bursts out
laughing.*

BAPTISTE : I love your laugh.

GARANCE : So do I . . . *Laughing* . . . What would I do without it?

BAPTISTE *seriously* : And what would I do without you? *She looks at him, astonished.* Tell me your name?

GARANCE : Garance.

BAPTISTE *dreamily* : Garance!

GARANCE *staring at him* : But you're trembling. Are you cold?

Close-up of BAPTISTE *full face,* GARANCE *half out of shot.*

BAPTISTE : I'm trembling because I'm happy . . . and I'm happy because you are there . . . close to me . . . I love you . . . and you, Garance . . . do you love me?

Reverse shot. GARANCE *puts her hand on* BAPTISTE'S *shoulder.*

GARANCE *disturbed* : You talk like a child . . .

She caresses his hair, as he had caressed NATALIE'S.

GARANCE : In books people love like that, and in dreams — but in life! . . .

BAPTISTE, *full face, in medium close-up, and* GARANCE *back view, half out of shot.*

BAPTISTE *interrupting her abruptly* : Dreams and life are the same — or else it's not worth living. And then . . . what do you think I care about life? It's not life I love, it's you!

GARANCE *more and more disturbed, close-up* : You are the sweetest boy I've ever met. *Leaning her face close to his.* I won't forget tonight, either. *Lowering her voice.* I like you very much.

BAPTISTE : I love you.

They kiss. Then close-up of BAPTISTE. *The two faces separate.*

BAPTISTE *enraptured* : Garance!

GARANCE *camera on her, who, sure of herself, pulls him towards her again* : Love is so simple! (*Still on page 74*)

They kiss again.

Medium long shot of them against the wall, their silhouettes mingling. Suddenly, a flash of lightning lights up the sky, . . . followed by a violent clap of thunder. GARANCE *and* BAPTISTE *separate suddenly.*

GARANCE : Heavens, a thunderstorm.

BAPTISTE, *shocked out of his trance of love, looks at the sky, then . . .*

BAPTISTE : If it rains you'll get soaked, Garance!

GARANCE : What does that matter?

BAPTISTE : Your clothes are so thin . . . Come on, come on, I'll take you back.

GARANCE : Where to?

BAPTISTE : To your home.

GARANCE : Home! *She bursts out laughing.* I haven't got a home!

BAPTISTE *medium close-up, full face* : Ah! . . .

> GARANCE *full face,* BAPTISTE *half out of shot. Then series of reverse angle shots.*

GARANCE *still smiling* : Yes . . . I left my job, and the job and the room . . . they went together. So!

BAPTISTE : If you like . . . where I live . . . I could find you a room . . .

GARANCE *looking at him with a tender smile* : A room?

BAPTISTE *not understanding* : Yes . . . Please, come on.

> *Long shot: the length of the road.* GARANCE *and* BAPTISTE *from the back, disappearing rapidly. Suddenly a heavy rain begins to fall. They run.*
>
> *Medium shot of the* OLD CLOTHES MAN *who comes out of a little street where he has been spying on the couple, and follows them.*
>
> [*A market gardener's cart turns into the street in the background . . .* GARANCE *and* BAPTISTE *turn the corner of the road. Shot of the cart, the rain beating against the horse's flanks, the storm lamp shaking in rhythm with the swaying of the cart, the driver asleep. The camera pans to follow the cart. Behind it can be seen for a fleeting instant the* OLD CLOTHES MAN *who rushes off in pursuit of* GARANCE *and* BAPTISTE. *Long shot of the road stretching away. The* OLD CLOTHES MAN *rapidly turns the corner. The road stays empty under the rain for a moment. The sound of a clock striking two can be heard from a house. The beat of the dance music, which had been scarcely audible as music at all, ends.*]
>
> (Cut during the shooting.)
>
> *That same night — the interior of the* 'Grand Relais'. *The rain is over, but everything is still running with water in the moonlight. Noise of water running and dripping from the gutters. Medium shot oriented towards the stairs leading to the rooms.*

BAPTISTE *off* : Madame Hermine!

The camera pans towards the foot of the stairs where BAP-
TISTE *and* GARANCE *stand, soaked to the skin.* GARANCE *is
wearing* BAPTISTE'S *jacket over her shoulders.*

BAPTISTE *louder* : Madame Hermine.

GARANCE *speaking softly* : Look here, you don't want to wake up
everybody, just for a room.

BAPTISTE : Where can she be? *He starts to call again.* Madame
Hermine!

Slight shot from below to frame MADAME HERMINE *as she
comes downstairs to their level.*

MME. HERMINE : Ah . . . it's you, Monsieur Baptiste. What's
happened? *She quickly buttons up her blouse, and sees* GARANCE.
Mademoiselle . . . *Embarrassed, to* BAPTISTE . . . Excuse me, I
was upstairs . . . Yes . . . *She smiles* . . . Someone was ill, nothing
serious, luckily. What can I do for you, Monsieur Baptiste?

BAPTISTE : I would like a room for Mademoiselle, who was caught
in the rain.

MME. HERMINE ' *understanding* ', *looking* GARANCE *up and down*:
Yes, of course, caught in the rain. *To* BAPTISTE *in a low voice.*
She's charming. Well, show her number ten on the second floor.
That's very convenient — I've left the key in the door. *She holds
out a lamp to* BAPTISTE. Good night, . . . *With a knowing smile*
. . . and sweet dreams.

BAPTISTE takes the lamp out of MADAME HERMINE'S *hands,
he and* GARANCE *pass in front of her, and go out, left. The
camera stays on* MME. HERMINE *who follows the couple with
her eyes.*

MME. HERMINE *languorously, half under her breath* : ' Silent and
furtive, like a cat in the night.'

*The corridor of the first floor. The couple walk towards the
camera.* BAPTISTE *stands aside to let* GARANCE *enter the room.
The camera pans to follow them.*

In GARANCE'S *room — medium shot,* BAPTISTE *puts the lamp
down on the table, and comes towards* GARANCE. *He takes
the jacket off her shoulders.*

BAPTISTE : How wet you are, Garance.

GARANCE *going towards the bed* : It's nothing. The storm is over.
I'll put my dress on the windowsill, and it will dry when the sun
comes up.

She begins to undo her dress. Medium shot of BAPTISTE *close to the table and looking at her, out of shot. Cut back to* GARANCE, *who smiles. Quick cut to him, horrified. Cut back to her as she continues to undo her bodice with the greatest simplicity. (Still on page 75)*

GARANCE *ironic, but tender at the same time* : Turn round, if you're embarrassed. *Cut back to* BAPTISTE *who obeys immediately.*

GARANCE *off* : It's not bad here, but a bit sad all the same.

BAPTISTE *back view* : Why sad?

GARANCE *off*: It's always sad, a room, when one sleeps alone. There — there we are. You can turn round now.

> BAPTISTE *turns round and sees . . .*
> *Medium shot of* GARANCE *with the counterpane wrapped round her like a sari. Her dress, stockings and underclothes are laid neatly over the back of a chair. She smiles at him. Cut back to* BAPTISTE *who studies her.*

GARANCE *camera on her — smiling* : Pretty costume, isn't it? One would think one was in India !

> *Cut back to* BAPTISTE, *dazzled.*

BAPTISTE : How beautiful you are !

> *He takes his jacket, his hat, and walks backwards towards the door, without taking his eyes off her.*

BAPTISTE : But I must let you sleep, Garance.

GARANCE *the camera on her, as she sits on the bed, looking at him*: I'm not really very sleepy.

BAPTISTE *camera on him* : Don't forget what I told you. If you want, you can work at the ' Funambules '.

GARANCE *naïvely* : But I don't know how to do anything.

BAPTISTE : I'll help you. You must have a job.

GARANCE : Well, why not. *Smiling.* I can show my legs — perhaps they'll like that . . .

> *She holds out one leg, delicately, and pulls the counterpane up a little way, to gaze at herself with respectful interest.*

GARANCE : At least audiences aren't all that complicated.

> BAPTISTE *comes into shot and sits down beside her on the bed. Close-up of the two.*

BAPTISTE : But Garance, I love you !

GARANCE *taking his hand* : Please, Baptiste, don't be so serious. You chill my heart. *Very gentle.* You mustn't be angry with me but I'm not . . . well, not how you dreamed of me. You must understand me — I'm simple — very simple . . . *She stands up beside him, lowering her voice* . . . I can't help being the way I am. I like people I like to like me. That's all. *With a very tender, gentle smile.* And when I want to say yes, I never learned how to say no.

She moves away from him, and approaches the table on the right, the camera panning to follow her. She blows out the lamp, so that the room is only lit by moonlight.

GARANCE : I like moonlight, don't you?

Pan to frame BAPTISTE *sitting on the bed facing the camera in slightly high angle shot, from her point of view.*

BAPTISTE *dreamily* : The moon, of course . . . the moon! *Sad laugh.* The moon is my country! *Half under his breath but with a harsh bitter tone, he repeats his father's words.* ' This one isn't one of ours. He's not like us. One night when the moon was full, he fell . . .' That's all! *Shaking his head; still imitating the voice of ' the others '.* ' He can't understand anything. He dreams of impossible things.' *Close-up of him as he gets up suddenly, almost in physical pain — very excited.* But why impossible, because I dream them — ' these things ' . . .

Medium close-up and pan — he comes towards GARANCE *and takes her in his arms.*

BAPTISTE : Oh, Garance, you can't realise! I wish, oh, I wish so much that you loved me as I love you!

Overcome, he is about to kiss her. She holds up her face. He dares not, turns aside his head and runs. The door slams, off, and the camera stays on GARANCE'S *face, shocked and distressed. Close-up of her, at first absolutely stunned. She stares at the door which* BAPTISTE *has just closed behind him. Then she shakes her head gently, with a smile, sad — but not too sad.*

[BAPTISTE'S *room — that same night. This room is very clean too, but much smaller and poorer than the other one and very untidy. A large mirror is balanced on a chair, which itself is balanced on an old trunk. On the walls, theatrical masks and costumes are hung, and on the furniture are piles of books.* BAPTISTE *walks abruptly into the room. He hesitates a moment, then he shuts the door behind him.*] (This shot was probably shot, but cut in the editing. We never see this room in the film.)

FREDERICK'S *room — very early the next morning.* FREDERICK, *wrapped in an old dressing gown, is stretched out on the bed. He is reading aloud in a low voice, but acting out what he reads, as he smokes his pipe.*

FREDERICK *reading :*

> ' . . . Yet I'll not shed her blood,
> Nor scar that whiter skin of hers than snow,
> And smooth as monumental alabaster :
> Yet she must die, else she'll betray more men.
> Put out the light, and then put out the light . . .'

Yes, that's it . . . put out the light and sleep. Good night, Desdemona. Good night, Othello.

He kisses the book, shuts it, and puts it on the night table; gets up, the camera panning to follow him, and just as he is going to blow out the lamp, he hears a feminine voice, coming from outside, singing, very simply, like children who put to any tune that comes into their head the words that happen to be passing through their mind.

[GARANCE *off — singing :*

> I am what I am,
> I drink when I thirst,
> And when I want to laugh,
> I laugh fit to burst !]

The camera tracks sideways to follow FREDERICK *who leaps over to the window.*

Track in to close-up of FREDERICK, *facing the camera, leaning on the balcony. What he sees enchants him. The voice is still singing.*

[GARANCE *off — singing :*

> Whom I love I embrace,
> And I take no blame
> If each loving face,
> Isn't the same.]

This song, both music and words (in French) by Prévert, is not sung in the film but only hummed, though the song became very well-known a few years later.)

FREDERICK *unable to believe his eyes :* Garance !

The window of GARANCE'S *room as seen by* FREDERICK. *A*

90

naked arm is quickly pulled out of sight, and only the dress and underclothes hanging on the rail of the balcony and swaying in the wind are visible.

FREDERICK *off — calling gently* : Hey, Garance!

GARANCE appears in the window, wearing her counterpane. He is half out of shot in the foreground.

GARANCE *surprised and smiling* : Frederick!

FREDERICK *gallant* : Pretty costume . . . but I preferred the other!

GARANCE : Nature allows for all tastes!

FREDERICK : Exactly!

GARANCE : How did you get here? Do you live here?

FREDERICK : Yes . . .

GARANCE : Well, I must say, for a chance meeting, this is quite a chance meeting!

Reverse angle shot: FREDERICK full face, and GARANCE leaning on her balcony, seen three-quarters view from the back, half out of shot.

FREDERICK *ironic and tender* : ' Paris is very small for those who love each other with such a grand passion.' *Suddenly.* You're alone, I hope?

GARANCE *with a sigh, close-up of her* : Alas, yes . . . all alone — I've been left to do penance.

Reverse angle of FREDERICK in medium close-up, then series of reverse angle close shots favouring the one who is speaking.

FREDERICK : Poor Garance, and aren't you frightened, all alone at night?

GARANCE : Oh, the sun will soon be up. He's an early riser, you know, the sun!

FREDERICK *off, camera on her* : And you?

GARANCE *evasive* : Oh . . . me!

FREDERICK *camera on him* : And then, after all, what does it matter, if the sun rises ' before us ', we will shut the shutters! *Suddenly with tender briskness.* And your door, my love, have you locked it?

GARANCE *smiling, in close shot* : I'm not afraid of burglars. What could they take from me?

She has hardly finished speaking when she starts with surprise. Close-up of FREDERICK's window — empty. Close-up of GAR- ANCE who turns round, smiling and dreamy, then suddenly turns

91

towards the interior of the room. The camera tracks forward to reveal the inside of the room; the door opens, FREDERICK *appears, and shuts it behind him, smiling tenderly towards* GARANCE *who stands motionless in the foreground.*
Fade out.

Outside it is day. Slightly high angle shot of the façade of the ' Theatre des Funambules', *the open air stage in front of the theatre, and a crowd of spectators seen from the back. On the platform* ANSELME DEBUREAU, *waxing more rapturous every minute, gives his spiel; there are more artistes in the parade than there were the first time — some are dressed in picturesque animal costumes, some as devils and she-devils, witches and sorcerers. (Still on page 76)*

ANSELME *continuing his spiel*: The incomparable Baptiste, my own son, of whom his father can be justly proud, has invented the entire spectacle we are going to present to you today. ' The Palace of Visions ' or the ' Lovers of the Moon '. *Medium shot of* DEBUREAU, *from the front, but behind his parade — he is shouting* . . .Unprecedented at this theatre, this show, ladies and gentlemen, has been running for more than three weeks before a more select audience every day, and without an excessive increase in the price of tickets. One franc fifty in the stage boxes, and thirty cents in the Gods ! *Fade out.*

The auditorium of the ' Theatre des Funambules'. *Long shot of the crowded auditorium, seen from the stage. Then medium shot of the stage seen from the stalls. The décor, painted with charming simplicity, is a park. In the middle of the park is a statue — it is a statue of Phoebe, Goddess of the Moon. Four children pass by, dancing in a circle; then a nursemaid, pushing a pram. Very sentimental music. Tracking shot, from a crane, plus gradual pan to frame a stage box in close-up. Three dandies, dressed with extravagant elegance, settle themselves in, and have eyes only for something on the stage.*

Cut to medium shot of the statue, which turns out to be none other than GARANCE. *Cut back to the box; the dandy in the centre, slightly older than the others, seems to be the most important. He is about forty, very phlegmatic, and without a doubt accustomed to being heard and obeyed. It is the* COUNT. *He makes a gesture with his head towards the stage.*

THE COUNT, *his voice trembling with contained emotion* : Look at her, George, just look! Have you ever seen a more splendid creature?

Medium shot of the statue of Phoebe — GARANCE, and cut back to the box.

GEORGE *smug and precious, adjusting his lorgnettes* : She's too divine, too utterly divine!

THE OTHER *smiling* : Well, my dear Edward, now I know where you pass your evenings!

GEORGE *even more affected* : And your nights!

THE COUNT *still looking to the stage* : You are mistaken, George, as usual.

He lights a very pretty clay pipe.

THE COUNT : I have never addressed a word to that young woman.

GEORGE : Really, Edward, but it's incredible!

THE COUNT : Perhaps, but it's the absolute truth : I haven't dared!

The two dandies stare at each other absolutely dumbfounded. The COUNT puts his monocle into his eye and stares attentively at the stage. Quick cut to GARANCE as the statue, then medium long shot of the stage, shot slightly from above. BAPTISTE, dressed in a white Pierrot's costume, enters, and approaches the statue. Applause. He is playing with a butterfly net.

Medium shot of the Gods who are applauding fit to burst. Among the spectators FIL DE SOIE cries jovially.

FIL DE SOIE *shouting* : Hello, Baptiste!

Cut to the stage. BAPTISTE is chasing a butterfly, but stops suddenly, struck by the beauty of the statue. Cut back to FIL DE SOIE, medium shot, full face.

[FIL DE SOIE *to his neighbours with obvious pride* : I can call him Baptiste, because I know him . . . he's a friend!] (Cut in final version.)

Medium shot of BAPTISTE walking round the statue; he has obviously fallen in love with it. He mimes ' the burning passion that grips him.' A PARK KEEPER appears. Intrigued by the unusual antics of BAPTISTE he watches him, and comes nearer. BAPTISTE has now leaned his head against the statue, and is almost embracing it. The PARK KEEPER comes nearer and stares threateningly at him right under his nose. BAPTISTE takes fright, apologises, explains that he is absolutely innocent, that he just happened to be taking a walk like that . . . and finally, he stumbles over a stone, falls down, and rolls off-stage. General laughter, and a pan across the audience seen from the stage.

[Medium shot of Mme. Hermine, *sitting in the stalls, facing the camera. Happy and proud she tells one of her neighbours.*
Mme. Hermine : He lives at my house, he's my lodger . . . and so is Monsieur Frederick.] (Cut in the versions released.)

Medium long shot of the stage: reassured, the Park Keeper *has turned his back and left the stage. Pan to the garden entrance —* Baptiste *re-enters, and from a distance, blows a kiss to the statue. In his hand he is carrying a big bouquet of flowers. Quick cut to the stage box, with* The Count *in close shot. Cut back to* Baptiste *who pricks a finger on a thorn on one of his flowers. He jumps. Laughter from the audience.* Baptiste *advances towards his idol, waving his bouquet. Medium close-up of* Garance *the statue, immobile, with no reaction. Medium close-up of* Baptiste, *facing the camera, miming surprise, and then distress. He makes another effort — cut back to* Garance *— the same thing. Cut back to medium long shot of* Baptiste *in despair. He sits down at the feet of the statue, the bouquet in his arms, and goes to sleep. Applause.*

In the wings: close-up of Anselme Debureau *and the* Director *watching the stage.*

Anselme *shaking the* Director : I tell you — the same laurels that decorate the head of the father have grown overnight on the forehead of my son! What a prodigious family!

Director *with a gesture towards the stage* : And what about him? You don't think that he's prodigious too?

Medium shot of the stage from their point of view; the wings are almost out of shot. Frederick *comes on stage skipping and jumping, then he dances right up to the statue, light, attractive, debonair. Long shot of the stage seen from the audience. He is wearing a beautiful Harlequin's costume . . . and a guitar over his shoulder. He starts to play his guitar at the feet of the statue . . . without deigning to pay any attention to poor sleeping* Baptiste. *(Still on page 76) Guitar music is heard above the other instruments in the orchestra. Cut back*

94

to a close-up of Debureau *and the* Director.

Anselme *contemptuous* : Well, he's obviously got some talent . . .
Shaking his head . . . but he's not a mime!

Director : What is he then?

Anselme *with a majestic grimace of contempt* : He's an actor! . . .
Medium long shot of the stage as seen from the audience:
Harlequin, *the statue and* Baptiste. Harlequin *plays his
guitar to the motionless statue.* Baptiste, *still dreaming,
nods his head to the sound of the guitar. Medium close-up
of the statue of* Phoebe *in profile, and* Harlequin, *shot from
above, close to her, with an expression at once supplicating
and sprightly. Suddenly the statue's eyes move, and she
smiles at* Harlequin. *Medium shot of the three of them seen
from the audience:* Harlequin, *wild with delight, jumps for
joy, and skips up to the sleeping* Baptiste. *He sneaks away
the bouquet of flowers, and comes back to give it to the
statue. Her pedestal is slowly sinking to the ground. Once
she is on ground level she holds out her hand to* Harlequin.
*He offers her the bouquet. The statue walks, or rather glides,
while* Harlequin *dances around her; they go out slowly,
leaving* Baptiste *asleep by the empty pedestal. Quick shots
of the audience, especially the Gods, shouting with laughter
. . . because . . . high angle shot of the stage: the* Park
Keeper *appears again, and sees the empty pedestal and*
Baptiste *asleep. Furious, he hurls himself at* Baptiste *and
starts shaking him;* Baptiste *wakes from his dream still
bathed in delight, and kisses the hand of the* Park Keeper,
thinking it is Phoebe's. *He realises his mistake as the* Park
Keeper *jerks away, and seeing the empty pedestal tries to
escape. Chase sequence. Medium long shot of the Gods. The
audience applaud and shout* ' There he is ' — ' That way ' —
' No, the other way '. *Long shot of the stage, with the scene
going on in the background. The spectators are applauding.
The curtain falls. Shot of the stage box, and the three dandies
facing the camera. The* Count *applauds politely, but the other
two, obviously glad to let themselves go a bit, clap wildly.*

George *with that special intonation of a member of society giving
his opinion about a show, although no one has asked them for it* :
Bravo! Splendid!

95

THE OTHER : Yes, it's awfully good . . . awfully amusing.

GEORGE : Very droll. Really, these people are extraordinary, extraordinary . . .

Medium close-up of the COUNT, *full face, the others half out of shot. Distant, impassive, he does not take his eyes off the stage. The shadow of the curtain, which is being raised again, passes across his face, which thus appears better lit. The music starts again, and cut.*

The stage: cut on the same movement of the curtain as it finishes rising, while the CONDUCTOR *conducts the Orchestra. The décor has changed and now represents a cheerful, sunny countryside.* BAPTISTE *comes on from the right, sad, abandoned, touching, ridiculous. He reaches the centre of the stage, and at that moment, hears the guitar music. Suddenly his face lights up. He looks round for somewhere to climb so that he can see further, and notices a tree. He starts to climb. That is to say, he mimes a man climbing, while standing still, while behind him a piece of scenery, painted in trompe l'œil, descends as he ' climbs ', looking away into the distance, his hand shading his eyes. The guitar music comes closer.* BAPTISTE *still ' climbs ' . . . The backcloth, as it unrolls, reveals a pretty river in the background. On the river a boat comes into view, in it* PHOEBE *and* HARLEQUIN *gaze at each other tenderly: she is standing in the boat, and he is kneeling at her feet, his eyes raised towards her face. As soon as he sees the boat* BAPTISTE *starts to wave violently, and to ' climb ' down fast.*

Medium long shot of the audience seen from the footlights. The audience are fairly silent and still, watching the stage with deep interest.

Cut back to medium long shot of the stage: BAPTISTE *has come down, but the boat has disappeared.*

Medium shot of BAPTISTE *with his back to the camera, then facing, his face expressing profound disappointment.*

[*He takes a few steps forward. Suddenly, he rushes towards the river, about to throw himself in, but pauses a moment . . . cautiously feels the water with his toe, finds it too cold, and turns away.*] (This scene was mimed and filmed, but cut in the editing because the ' river ' had disappeared when he came down the tree.)

Medium long shot: BAPTISTE, *worn out, comes back to the centre of the stage . . . and sees a rope tied to a young sapling. He unties the rope, and too miserable to live, goes looking for a stronger tree to tie the rope to, walking straight ahead with the rope in his hand. In fact, he mimes the movements of walking, while the backcloth of the countryside slides past behind him, in the opposite direction. Medium close-up, then close-up of his legs and feet, walking on the spot. Cut back to long shot, then cut to close-up of the feet, then resume on a medium long shot: suddenly, a tree appears.* BAPTISTE *stops, throws the rope over the biggest branch, climbs onto a big stone . . . Pan, in medium shot, to reveal a* LITTLE GIRL *who is approaching smiling and full of the joys of spring . . . Pan back in the other direction to* BAPTISTE *again, who has not seen her because he is busy fixing his rope. The* LITTLE GIRL *pulls his sleeve, and 'asks' him to lend her the rope for a skipping rope.* BAPTISTE *agrees, against his will, and resigned to waiting, sits down on the big stone, while the* LITTLE GIRL, *all smiles, skips beside him. Suddenly, she decides she has had enough, gives back the rope and runs off.* BAPTISTE *watches her go sadly. He makes a gesture of 'adieu' with his hand, and turning back to his tree, he ties the rope up a second time. Pan, in medium shot, to reveal a pretty young* LAUNDRESS (NATALIE) *approaching happily, pushing a wheelbarrow full of washing. Pan in the opposite direction, and medium long shot; she stops a few yards away from the tree, sees* BAPTISTE, *and immediately asks if she can borrow his rope to dry her washing on.* BAPTISTE, *resigned again, but even sadder, ties the rope to a low branch, and as he is looking round vaguely holding the other end of the rope, for a place to fix it, the* LAUNDRESS, *smiling, signs to him to stay where he is. And he stays there, not knowing what else to do, holding the rope out in front of him. The* LAUNDRESS *hangs out her washing with little skips and jumps, taking no notice of* BAPTISTE *who holds the rope. Then she sits down on the wheelbarrow in front of the footlights, facing the audience, and taking a little mirror out of her pocket, she starts to do her hair.* BAPTISTE *stays where he is; stuck; rooted like a tree . . . when suddenly he hears the sound of the guitar again. He looks round to find out where it is coming from. Medium close-up of* BAPTISTE'S *face. (Still on page 109)*

[Series of close-ups of the tree, the washing, the rope, and the LAUNDRESS, *titivating her hair.]* (These shots filmed but cut in the versions shown.)

Medium close-up of BAPTISTE. *His face expresses real distress, absolute despair; in fact, he is looking into the wings.*

Shot of the wings, as seen by BAPTISTE. GARANCE *and* FREDERICK, *standing very close to one another, look into each other's eyes, smiling and talking.*

Cut back to BAPTISTE *in despair.*

Medium close-up of NATALIE *who starts up abruptly, ' feeling ' something wrong. She turns towards* BAPTISTE. *Cut to* BAPTISTE, *more and more wretched. Cut back to* NATALIE, *overwhelmed to see* BAPTISTE *suffering so; she cannot stop herself from crying out —*

NATALIE *crying* : Baptiste !

Medium close-up of the musicians, as seen from the stage: at the sound of NATALIE'S *voice they hesitate for a moment, and look at one another, astonished.*

Medium long shot of the stage, shot slightly from below, as seen from the audience: NATALIE *and* BAPTISTE. *Embarrassed,* NATALIE *turns round towards the audience. Long shot of the audience, who are muttering among themselves. Cut back to the stage where* NATALIE *takes up her role as* LAUNDRESS *again, and starts to scold* BAPTISTE *for not holding the rope straight.* BAPTISTE *in turn takes up the story.*

In the wings, the DIRECTOR *rushes forward from backstage to join the stupefied* STAGE MANAGER *and* ANSELME DEBUREAU, *paralysed with indignation in the foreground.*

DIRECTOR *beside himself* : Somebody cried out, spoke on stage ! Three francs fine . . . no five francs ! *Suddenly.* Who was it ?

ANSELME DEBUREAU *solemnly* : It was Natalie !

DIRECTOR *scarlet with rage* : My daughter ! . . . *to the* STAGE MANAGER . . . well, only three francs.

Just then, NATALIE, *coming off stage, comes into shot with her back to the camera, passes by the group and walks away. The* DIRECTOR *rushes after her. The camera follows him to frame them both in close-up.*

DIRECTOR : Natalie, are you out of your mind? Why did you cry out? You know perfectly well that it's forbidden. Do you want me to have to close the theatre? Come on now, Natalie, at least tell me why.

Medium close up of the two of them: NATALIE *facing the camera, her* FATHER *three-quarters backview.*

NATALIE : Because I was afraid!

DIRECTOR *astonished* : Afraid of what?

NATALIE : It was Baptiste who frightened me. *Lowering her voice.* . . . who still frightens me.

The STAGE MANAGER *and* ANSELME DEBUREAU, *who have approached while* NATALIE *has been speaking, look at one another in surprise. Close-up of the group. Seeing their surprise,* NATALIE *facing the camera continues.*

NATALIE : So you don't understand anything, you don't feel anything, you don't see anything? Don't you see that Baptiste has changed? That he's no longer the same person? Don't you see how he looks at you now, as if he doesn't see you? As if he was lost . . . lost forever?

Close-up of the group facing the camera, with NATALIE *in profile.*

ANSELME DEBUREAU *intervening* : Really, Natalie, I think you must be losing your mind. *Close-up of her, he continues off.* On the contrary, Baptiste has never been so gay, so wide awake. *Cut back to him, suddenly pompous and assertive.* Anyway, I think I should know him better than you, after all, I am his father!

Applause off, probably as BAPTISTE *exits. Medium close-up of* NATALIE *facing the camera, the others partly out of shot, backview or sideview.*

NATALIE : You know him, perhaps; but I love him, and I can see that he is in despair. And the rope. It was his idea, the rope.

Pan to reveal, in close-up, BAPTISTE *who approaches the group and pan back quickly to take in the whole group again.* BAPTISTE *puts an affectionate hand on* NATALIE's *shoulder. Shot of all four:* BAPTISTE, NATALIE, *the* DIRECTOR *and* ANSELME.

BAPTISTE *with a gentle smile* : And wasn't it a good idea?

DIRECTOR *raising his arms to heaven* : A marvellous idea!

ANSELME DEBUREAU *pointing to* BAPTISTE : A magnificent idea, and worthy of the son of his father.

BAPTISTE *smiling* : My father who beat me like a jelly to teach me the trade . . . and who said . . .

ANSELME DEBUREAU *close-up, as he interrupts emphatically* : A kick in the pants, when it's well delivered, can make the whole world laugh! And it's true! There's a whole gamut, a science, a style of kicks in the pants. But alas, the old traditions die . . . the public always want something new. *He looks round — everyone has gone.* Something new! Some novelty. *He shrugs his shoulders as he, too, goes off.* It's as old as the world itself — novelty!

> *Medium shot of* NATALIE *and* BAPTISTE. *The camera tracks to follow them into the wings; they are walking slowly.* NATALIE *starts up the little spiral staircase.* BAPTISTE *stays down below, near the footlights.* NATALIE *stops on the third step; she turns to look at* BAPTISTE.

BAPTISTE *still very calm, and smiling with a tight smile* : Despair means nothing, Natalie. Are you in despair?

NATALIE : Oh, it's not the same for me.

BAPTISTE : Why not?

NATALIE : Because I'm sure that everything will turn out right in the end.

BAPTISTE : You think that everything will turn out all right?

NATALIE : Yes, I have hope. At least I hope that perhaps, one day, in spite of everything, you will love me.

> *She sits on the steps and stares at him intently through the rails of the bannisters. Medium close-up of her, with* BAPTISTE *in the foreground, backview, and half out of shot.*

BAPTISTE *touched* : You are sweet, Natalie.

NATALIE : So are you, Baptiste. It's not our fault, what has happened. . . *shaking her head* . . . but all the same, it's stupid, it's badly arranged, we're going round like circus horses. I love you and you don't love me, and you love Garance and Garance loves Frederick!

> *Medium close-up of* BAPTISTE, *slightly high angle, as seen by her, she backview and half out of shot. Then series of shots from below.*

BAPTISTE : How do you know? Why do you say that Garance loves Frederick?

NATALIE: I don't know really, but I mean, I thought so. *Very naïve.* Because they are living together.

BAPTISTE *with sudden, sombre exaltation*: What does that prove, Natalie? . . . Nothing. If all the people who lived together loved each other, the earth would shine like the sun.

NATALIE *sad*: Baptiste!

[*Medium shot and pan with* FREDERICK *as he comes past.*

FREDERICK: Where's the director, I want to speak to him. *He sees* NATALIE *and* BAPTISTE. Long live love, nobody's bored here! *With a grand gesture.* Enjoy yourselves, children . . . make the most of life — *Taken up with his idea again, he goes out, muttering.* Where's the Director? . . . Where is he?] (Cut in released versions.)

> *Cut back to close-up of* BAPTISTE *and* NATALIE. BAPTISTE *is sad and quiet, watching* FREDERICK *walk away. He takes* NATALIE'S *arm.*

BAPTISTE: Believe me, Natalie, they don't live together, they pretend to live!

> *Another corner of the wings: close-up of* FREDERICK *approaching the* DIRECTOR.

FREDERICK: Ah! Here he is!

DIRECTOR *turning round*: What is it?

> FREDERICK *takes the* DIRECTOR'S *arm and shakes it while he speaks, emphasising his words.*

FREDERICK *his voice getting higher and higher as he continues*: What's the matter? This is what's the matter. Frederick can't stand it any longer. You've put a gag in Frederick's mouth, and it's suffocating him!

DIRECTOR: Please don't shout so loud. The audience'll be able to hear you.

> FREDERICK *suddenly leaves the* DIRECTOR *and takes a few steps upstage. During the whole scene he walks rapidly to and fro like a caged animal, under the eyes of the* DIRECTOR *who is at first horrified, but then conciliating.*

FREDERICK: Nothing but contempt! Do you hear, Frederick, ' the audience'll be able to hear you '. *Suddenly shaking the* DIRECTOR. Do you want to make Frederick explode with your pantomime? Yes, die, from silence, like others die from hunger or thirst. *Shaking his head.* When I think that even when I was little, I wanted to climb into the pulpit and give the sermon instead of the priest!

THE DIRECTOR *being a good chap, and taking* FREDERICK'S *arm*: Come on, don't get cross. Just now, when I saw you coming, I was afraid you wanted a rise, and I've got so many expenses. But we can always arrange something for you. I know, if you want from time to time, I could put you outside with the parade. You could do the spiel. That'd be a little compensation, at least!

FREDERICK: The parade? Why not? *Starting to pace back and forward again.* I'd do anything, anywhere, rather than continue to play goldfish in front of an audience of deaf mutes! Anyone! Listen, I'd rather be a cripple and wheel myself round the streets singing ballads . . . or play at the Blind Hospital, in front of an audience who can't see! *With a noble gesture.* Ah! Joan of Arc was happy hearing voices. 'Voices'. . . I don't ask so much. If only I could hear my own occasionally, from time to time!

> *He waves his guitar, is about to explode again, but stops. He has seen someone.*
> *The camera tracks backwards in front of* GARANCE, *who is approaching in medium shot. She crosses the wings and turns.* FREDERICK *joins her, and the camera tracks sideways to follow them, and they talk as they walk.*

FREDERICK: Where have you been, Garance, my sweet bird of the evening? I was looking for you, I missed you. One moment without you and my heart stops beating.

> GARANCE *does not reply, and hardly smiles.*

FREDERICK: At last I have found the flower of my days, the light of my nights, my fair Iseult with black hair, my sweet and tender Iphigenia . . . my life and my love . . . who lightens all my burdens!

> GARANCE *stops, the camera with her, she looks at* FREDERICK *with a smile full of weariness.*

GARANCE: When you've finished, Frederick, let me know!

FREDERICK *still smiling and debonair*: Ungrateful creature — you want to silence the voice of love itself!

GARANCE *on the threshold of the dressing room*: What? *She turns towards him.* The voice of love itself?

> *She laughs, and goes into the dressing room.* FREDERICK *follows her.*
> *In the dressing room, that has already been seen, medium shot of* GARANCE. *She stares unhappily at* FREDERICK. *The*

102

camera pans to follow her as she goes to sit down, wearily, back to the camera, at her dressing table. FREDERICK *comes up beside her, and puts one foot on the bench on which* GARANCE *is sitting, as she begins to take off her make-up.*

FREDERICK *still smiling, but a little surprised* : What are you thinking, beautiful sphinx? (*Still on page 110*)

GARANCE *shot from above — he is half out of shot* : Nothing . . . a lot of things. Well, for instance, I'm thinking that there are, all over the world, lovers who love each other without saying anything, or who speak about their love with very simple words, everyday words. *Very simply.* I find that lovely.

FREDERICK : Aren't you happy with me, Garance?

GARANCE *shaking her head* : You're not happy with me, either, Frederick.

FREDERICK : Me!

He looks astonished, and comes to sit beside her. Medium close-up of the two of them, GARANCE *facing the camera, him with his back to it.*

GARANCE : If you were happy, would you make jokes all the time? If you thought that I was happy, would you try so desperately to keep me amused. *Shaking her head.* Neither happy, nor unhappy, we're somewhere between the two, that's all! We don't love each other — it's not our fault, of course, but all the same, Frederick, it's nothing to be so proud of!

FREDERICK, piqued, stands for a moment without saying anything, automatically caressing Phoebe's crescent moon in GARANCE's *hair with the tip of his finger.*

FREDERICK : ' A soft ray of moonlight on hair as dark as night.'

He smiles, and gentle but forceful, leans down towards her; he is now facing the camera, she still has her back to the camera and continues with her make-up.

FREDERICK : Perhaps you would like it — I don't know, if I was always going on at you, and asking questions, eh? If I made you tell me everything in your past, if I spied on you, watched you, followed you in the streets, from a distance, hugging the walls where I had written your name? If I woke you suddenly in the middle of the night to demand who you were dreaming about? *Stopping suddenly and smiling broadly.* That, at least, would be absolutely useless.

Series of close-ups shot from below, favouring the one who is speaking.

GARANCE *surprised* : Why?

FREDERICK : Because you talk in your sleep, my love.

GARANCE : Me? I talk in my sleep?

FREDERICK : Yes, my love. You were doing it last night, talking as you dreamed.

GARANCE *a bit worried — she begins to speak while the camera is still on* FREDERICK, *who watches her closely* : What did I say?

FREDERICK : Not much. . . . Baptiste!

GARANCE *shrugging her shoulders* : Me, I said Baptiste?

FREDERICK *off* : Yes, my love, you did!

GARANCE : What else did I say?

FREDERICK : Nothing. Just Baptiste.

GARANCE *reassured* : That's all!

Medium shot of FREDERICK *facing the camera and* GARANCE *backview and half out of shot. The camera pans and tracks backwards slightly to follow the movement as* FREDERICK *leaps up in one bound and mimes indignation and anger with clownish exaggeration.*

FREDERICK : What do you mean, that's all? Isn't it enough to reduce a heart like mine to despair? *Approaching her.* Do not forget, perfidious creature, that Othello killed Desdemona for much less than that. For nothing, do you hear? For nothing, Othello made himself a widower. For nothing, for a despicable little object, a mere handkerchief.

He moves away from her, and cannot resist making a bad pun, at which he alone laughs.

FREDERICK : A little batiste handkerchief, I'm sure!

Close-up of GARANCE, *facing the camera. She is looking at him with weary hostility.*

Medium long shot of FREDERICK, *facing the camera, he does not seem to notice the look* GARANCE *is giving him, and smiles as he pirouettes.*

FREDERICK : Yes . . . batiste!

The camera, panning and tracking very slightly forward follows FREDERICK *as he jumps and climbs the little staircase that leads to the door. The* STAGE MANAGER *comes in, still perturbed, stick in hand; he passes* FREDERICK *and comes towards* GARANCE.

STAGE MANAGER: Mademoiselle Garance, there's someone here who absolutely insists on seeing you !

Medium shot of the door, FREDERICK *is about to go out, but is prevented by a huge bouquet of flowers which fills the whole doorway as it comes in. Cut back to medium shot of* GARANCE, *she seems very surprised, and stares up at the* STAGE MANAGER.

GARANCE : What on earth are all these flowers? I don't believe it. Someone must be dead. *She gets up slowly as she speaks.*

Long shot of the dressing room shot slightly from above. The bouquet of flowers, carried by two little pages, is put down in the centre of the room in front of GARANCE *who has taken a few steps forward. The two pages leave, followed by the* STAGE MANAGER, *and then* FREDERICK. *The camera pauses for a second on the empty doorway which is immediately filled by the figure of* COUNT EDWARD, *who comes forward, hiding his embarrassment and emotion beneath an impressive calm. He comes down the steps stiffly, playing with his cane in one hand as he speaks.*

THE COUNT : Yes, Mademoiselle, someone is dead. A man who thought he was secure, who thought he understood himself. That man is dead, and you have killed him !

Close-up as he comes to the floral display and stops. GARANCE *is standing on the opposite side of the flowers.*

GARANCE *amused, but also a bit irritated* : Please, you're frightening me.

THE COUNT *facing the camera* : Don't be afraid; because of you, thanks to you . . . another man is born . . . a new man, who places his life in your hands.

Close-up of GARANCE, *alone, as she sits down again, near the flowers. She smiles.*

GARANCE : What do you expect me to do with it ?

THE COUNT : Whatever you like.

He approaches her, as she sits with her back to the dressing table. Close-up of the two of them. He remains standing.

THE COUNT : I make myself your prisoner. Yes, you can do what you like with me. *Becoming rather affected as he emphasises his words.* All that I possess, and I possess much, all that belongs to me, I lay at your feet.

He leans down, takes her hand and kisses it. The camera moves in to a close-up of GARANCE, *shot slightly from above. The* COUNT *is three-quarters back view, half out of the picture. She looks automatically at the* COUNT, *then at her hand. As he begins to speak he is partly out of shot.*

THE COUNT : Forgive me, Mademoiselle, but I have never been so moved, so overcome as I am at this moment. *Low angle shot from her point of view of the* COUNT *facing the camera.* I am expressing myself badly, I know. I repeat platitudes, trivialities. *Tilt down on her.* Anyway, what I say is of no importance ! *Cut back to him, feverish and excited.* What is important, is what you are going to reply to me. One word, Mademoiselle, and your life can change completely. *Cut back to her.* Tomorrow, if you wish, the most beautiful women, the toasts of Paris . . . *cut back to him . . .* will bite their lips till they run with blood, just to hear your name mentioned. Beside yours, their rarest jewels will be as dull as coal. You will have the most splendid carriage —

GARANCE *camera on her* : I'm frightened of horses.

THE COUNT *camera on him — abashed* : Oh, please, don't say no.

GARANCE *camera on her* : But why do you want me to say yes if it gives me no pleasure ?

THE COUNT *camera on him* : Say nothing then . . . let me hope !

Close-up of the two of them; as GARANCE *speaks, she gets up and goes over to her screen; the camera pans to follow her, always keeping him in shot.*

GARANCE : That's it; I'll be quiet, and you can talk away to yourself. And because you're moved, ' overcome ', you'll go on talking ' platitudes ' as you put it : diamonds, horses, bridles, hay and then the harness . . . you know, the grand life ! *She shrugs her shoulders.*

Close-up of the COUNT *facing the camera. More and more taken aback and upset, he walks a few steps without replying. The camera comes back to* GARANCE, *in close-up, as she goes behind her screen. Her face can hardly be seen. She undresses as she speaks, and hangs her costume over the edge of the screen. Cut back to the* COUNT *who sits down in a corner of the room on a basket, facing the screen as seen by her. (Still on page 110)*

106

GARANCE : Oh, if all that just fell from the skies and landed in my lap perhaps I wouldn't say no. But, all the same, that way of talking : ' One word and your whole life can change ' . . . I suppose that means that my life is nothing . . . you're trying to say that my life is nothing at all ! *He does not say a word, but seems to take in what she is saying, though he does not show it; she becomes more aggressive.* And what if I like my life, my own little life? I'm a big girl, after all; I know what I'm saying and I know what I'm doing. Whereas you, to look at you . . . *Cut back to her as she examines him coldly* . . . you may have a ' grand life ', but really, when one takes a good look at you, perhaps you are only a little man; a very little man.

> *Close-up of the* COUNT, *sitting, unperturbed, but slightly hurt all the same.*

THE COUNT : Never . . . you understand, never, has anybody ever spoken to me like that !

GARANCE *shot of her behind the screen, putting on a dress* : Nor to me, neither ! . . . You mustn't be cross, but all the same, you turn up, you decide what's going to be done with me, you make your inventory . . . you find me attractive . . . fine, everything's understood. *She stops for a moment and becomes dreamy.* But what if somebody loves me? (*Still on page 111*)

THE COUNT *airy and sure of himself* : There's no question of it. You are far too beautiful for anyone really to love you ! Beauty is an exception, an insult to the world . . . which is ugly ! It is exceedingly rare for a man to love beauty. They simply buy it so that they won't have to hear about it any more — to wipe it out and forget it.

GARANCE *off, she is hidden behind the screen* : Perhaps you're a hunter?

THE COUNT : Don't make a mistake, Mademoiselle. I meant every word that I said. I offered you a refuge, that is all !

> *Close-up of* GARANCE, *facing the camera as she comes round the edge of the screen buttoning the bodice of her dress.*

GARANCE : A refuge?

> *Medium shot of the* COUNT *playing with a cardboard roast chicken, one of the theatre props, which he has picked up. He is still sitting in his corner.*

THE COUNT : Yes. *Feverish and a bit pathetic.* I've changed. I regret it, there's no doubt about that, but there's nothing I can do about it. Since I first saw you, I find myself indulging in absurd, childish daydreams! *He gets up and paces up and down with a derisory little laugh.* Perhaps I've got older — or perhaps it's what's called a ' coup de foudre '. *Shaking his head in medium close-up.* I don't exist any longer. I'm reduced to nothing, bound hand and foot; I have no will of my own; I'm no more than air and cardboard — like this chicken.

> *He looks at the chicken, and laughs again, more bitterly. Medium shot, facing the camera.*

THE COUNT: A coup de foudre! . . .Yes! That's just what it is!

> *Suddenly and violently, he hurls the chicken towards the end of the room, with all his strength. The camera pans swiftly to follow the flight of the chicken in close-up as it hits the thunder sheet. There is a violent and prolonged clap of thunder. Medium long shot of* GARANCE *in her street clothes, facing the camera; long shot of the dressing room: they are facing each other, two or three yards apart.*

GARANCE: And that's a clap of thunder. Three francs fine. *She smiles.*

> *The* COUNT *comes closer.*

THE COUNT: Forgive me, Mademoiselle. I realise that I've been indiscreet, importunate . . .

> *In the background the* STAGE MANAGER *comes running in, mad with rage and stuttering threats.*

STAGE MANAGER: But . . . but . . . who made that thunder? The old man is furious!

> *High angle long shot of the room as seen by the* STAGE MANAGER; *he is half out of shot in the foreground.*

GARANCE *calm*: I did.

> *Medium shot of the* STAGE MANAGER *on the threshold.*

STAGE MANAGER *grumbling as he tries to calm down*: All right, all right . . . You know the tariff. That's three francs! *He goes out quickly.*

> *Close-up of the* COUNT *and* GARANCE.

GARANCE *ironic*: You owe me three francs!

> *The* COUNT *looks at her, speechless. She comes closer to him as she speaks. Pan in a slight curve to frame them again in medium close-up, one beside the other.*

GARANCE : But there's no hurry, I'm working at the moment, and I've got enough to live on!

THE COUNT *more and more disturbed* : Enough to live on! I hope you're telling the truth, Mademoiselle. But let me withdraw, and if I have seemed ridiculous to you, you mustn't judge me too harshly. Your beauty alone is the cause of my confusion. *With a sigh.* And I haven't even introduced myself yet!

> *Out of his waistcoat pocket he takes a card which he holds out to* GARANCE.

THE COUNT : It's incredible! *He bows and straightens himself as he declaims his identity.* Count Edward de Monteray. Please, Mademoiselle, keep my card. You never know. Misfortune doesn't always choose which door it knocks at, and one day you may need help, protection. In that case, and whatever happens, do not forget that I am your devoted slave, body and soul, and that you can have the most absolute confidence in me.

> *He bows again, one last time, and cold and phlegmatic, walks towards the door. The camera follows him: he climbs the stairs, and the camera reveals* BAPTISTE *who comes in and stares after this unusual visitor. The* COUNT, *ignoring him completely, goes out.*
>
> *The camera tracks backwards and then pauses to frame* GARANCE *in medium close-up, as she feels with her finger the engraving of a crown on the card.*

GARANCE *smiling, half under her breath* : Flowers! A crown! I said so, it's a funeral!

BAPTISTE, *the camera moves back in the opposite direction to frame him on the staircase* : Mine, perhaps.

GARANCE *medium long shot, from above* : Don't be silly. Baptiste. Why do you say that?

> BAPTISTE, *smiling, moves towards* GARANCE, *and prowls round her as he speaks, getting more and more irritable. The camera pans slightly to follow his comings and goings.*

BAPTISTE : And why shouldn't Baptiste have a funeral like everyone else? I assure you, Garance, I think of it quite often. Nice subject for a little sketch — Baptiste taking his secret with him to the grave!

GARANCE : Be quiet, Baptiste. It's silly to talk like that.

BAPTISTE *continuing* : My secret, Garance? That tiny glow? The

memory of one night when he thought himself happy for evermore.
She seems more and more distressed and ill-at-ease. He on the other hand becomes even more excited, shakes his fists in the air, and starts pacing up and down again.

BAPTISTE *continuing*: Oh! Don't look like that! *He laughs, and clowns for a few seconds.* When you come down to it, it's not really so sad, a funeral. All you need is a bit of sunshine, and everybody's happy. *Very close to her, and more and more jovial.* And then if you think about it, it's a lot gayer than a wedding night with the bridegroom all alone, and no bride!
He mimes it, embracing the empty air for the ' bride ', and stopping suddenly in front of the COUNT'S *flowers. The camera follows him;* GARANCE *is out of shot.*

BAPTISTE : I don't like this wedding bouquet!
He throws some of the flowers on the ground, and stamps on them, then suddenly overcome with rage he picks up a riding whip and violently lashes at the bouquet, which falls to pieces. (Still on page 112)

BAPTISTE *whipping the flowers*: I hate these flowers! I hate everybody . . . that man who was here.
The camera pans to frame GARANCE, *who looks very sad.*

GARANCE : Come on, Baptiste.

BAPTISTE *coming towards her*: I detest Frederick, I detest myself . . . I loathe myself!
His crisis seems to calm him. He is weary. He walks backwards, passing GARANCE, *with the camera following him, and stops in front of a mirror.*

BAPTISTE *bursting out laughing in front of the mirror*: Baptiste? What is he? Baptiste, since the one he loves doesn't love him. A nothing, a will o' the wisp . . . *He mimes it* . . . A machine man . . . *He mimes it.* A were wolf. *He laughs even louder, he mimes.* End of Baptiste . . .
Suddenly he sticks his finger in a pot of make-up and draws a cross on the mirror.

BAPTISTE : That's the end of Baptiste. Here lies Baptiste . . .*very upset* . . . Life gave him only a red flower, a good thrashing and a wooden overcoat!
[And BAPTISTE *draws his epitaph with his finger on the mirror. Close-up of the mirror:* BAPTISTE'S *finger draws:* ' Here lies

Baptiste.' *Close-up of* GARANCE, *distressed. She is looking at* BAPTISTE. *Close-up of the mirror;* BAPTISTE's *finger finishes the epitaph.*

> *Here lies Baptiste*
> *Life gave him only*
> *a red flower*
> *a good thrashing*
> *and a wooden overcoat . . .*

But hardly has BAPTISTE's *hand finished writing the last word when another hand rubs out the epitaph.*] (In the final versions the epitaph was spoken because writing it out took too long.)

Fade out.

Medium close-up of BAPTISTE *and* GARANCE *facing the camera. She comes close to* BAPTISTE *and smiles at him. He is sitting, crushed and wretched, at the dressing table. He sits up straight.*

GARANCE : Baptiste, who says that I don't love you?

NATALIE *off, in a loud voice* : I say so.

BAPTISTE *and* GARANCE *turn round . . . Medium shot to frame* NATALIE *facing the camera: she has come in without the others noticing. She stands motionless, hard and cold. During the following dialogue a series of reverse angle shots between the couple and* NATALIE.

GARANCE *astonished* : What do you know about it?

NATALIE *very innocent and straightforward* : Everything to do with Baptiste, I know, I see, I understand, I guess!

BAPTISTE : Natalie, I forbid you!

NATALIE : That's the way it is, it's true. You don't know anything about it, so be quiet. *To* GARANCE. Of course, I don't mean that you're lying, but I know. *Very sure of herself and then suddenly very passionate.* Yes, I know that all the love that there is in the world for Baptiste is mine, do you hear? It's mine . . . There's no room for anyone else. It's written down. It's fate. *Quick cut to* GARANCE. I've taken it all, I know. *Cut back to* NATALIE. It's one of the things which . . . is! *Quick cut to* GARANCE, *who smiles.* Oh! You can smile!

GARANCE *with no hostility* : I always smile.

NATALIE : You're lucky; I hardly ever smile any more. *To* BAP-

115

TISTE. And nor do you, Baptiste. You who were so gay . . . who thought of nothing but your work.

BAPTISTE *suddenly interrupting her, seized with a cold rage*: That's enough, Natalie. Leave me — leave us alone. Go away. Do you hear? Go away.

> *He walks abruptly out of shot. The camera picks him up again with a short pan as he goes up to* NATALIE, *in close-up, and shakes her roughly, repeating.*

BAPTISTE: Go away!

> NATALIE *looks at* GARANCE, *off.*

NATALIE *to* GARANCE: It's because of you that he speaks to me like this. *Shaking her head.* Forgive me for saying all that; it's not only that I'm jealous, but I'm so sure. *Radiant.* Yes. I am sure that Baptiste and I are made to live together.

> NATALIE *pulls herself free from* BAPTISTE *and runs out. The camera remains on* BAPTISTE, *who turns slowly to* GARANCE *out of shot, and looks at her sadly. Reverse angle shot of* GARANCE *embarrassed, lowering her eyes. Dissolve.*
>
> *The ground floor of the ' Grand Relais '. It is daytime. The window of a room seen from the outside.* LACENAIRE, *half hidden behind it, looks out towards the street. Shot from above from his point of view. The courtyard;* MME. HERMINE'S *room is in the background, to the left. She is standing on the threshold talking to a* NEIGHBOUR. *A* DEBT COLLECTOR *arrives, and nods to her, then looks in his satchel for a piece of paper. Through an open window someone can be heard playing scales on a violin — very badly. Almost inaudible in final version.*
>
> *Cut back to the first window in medium close-up.* LACENAIRE *has disappeared.*
>
> *Cut back to a close-up shot from above, then a medium shot of the* DEBT COLLECTOR *who is addressing* MME. HERMINE.

DEBT COLLECTOR: Monsieur Forestier?

MME. HERMINE *pointing*: On the first floor, at the bottom of the courtyard.

DEBT COLLECTOR: Thank you.

> *The* DEBT COLLECTOR *goes off down the courtyard while the two women continue to chat.*
>
> LACENAIRE'S *apartment.*

116

Shot of Lacenaire *who has left the window and is going briskly over to the door. The camera pans to show the apartment which is almost empty. In the right foreground there is a large white wicker-work trunk.* Avril *is standing in the centre of the room, leaning against the table, which is covered with a plush table cloth.*

Lacenaire : Here we are, get ready. Our prey is almost here.

He hands Avril *a heavy object wrapped in a cloth, as he gives a significant look towards the trunk.*

Lacenaire : The game bag is ready . . . Perfect!

Avril *a bit pale* : You give me cold shivers down the spine, Monsieur Lacenaire!

Avril *moves towards an alcove on the left, while* Lacenaire *goes quickly over to the door at the far end of the room. When he is just a step away he turns round one last time towards* Avril.

Lacenaire : So, you know what you've got to do. He knocks, I open, you give him a couple of knocks in turn . . . *touching the interior of his jacket with his hand* . . . and if necessary, I'll finish things off!

Avril *nods in agreement, while* Lacenaire *hides behind the door, listening.*

In the courtyard of the ' Grand Relais ', *a medium shot of* Mme. Hermine *and her* Neighbour. *In the background the* Debt Collector *can be seen slowly climbing the staircase.* [*Some children are playing in the puddles between the paving stones.*] (In the script, but not shot because the weather was sunny.) *The* Neighbour *is knitting as she talks. They are both standing in front of the doorway.*

Mme. Hermine *gesturing towards the* Debt Collector : He's lucky — Monsieur Forestier's hardly ever in. He's waiting for his furniture, which is in the country. And in the two weeks since he rented that apartment this is only the second time that I've seen him.

Neighbour : What's he like?

Mme. Hermine *her eyes shining* : A perfect gentleman . . . so distinguished! *Suddenly.* What surprises me is that he was recommended by Mademoiselle Garance!

Neighbour : You don't like her, eh? . . . *Picking up a dropped*

117

stitch . . . Mademoiselle Garance?

MME. HERMINE *very dignified* : I don't deign to notice her existence. *Shaking her head.* Really, when I think of the way she twists poor Monsieur Frederick round her little finger. *With another sigh.* Well . . . I'm glad I've managed to let that little apartment on the first floor! It'll be nice to have someone well-bred in the house for a change!

At that moment, someone can be heard screaming.

DEBT COLLECTOR *off* : Murderers! . . . Cut throats! . . .

(N.B. The script mentions that the violin stops here — though it is not noticeable in the finished version.)

General shot of the courtyard from the women's point of view. LACENAIRE and AVRIL appear immediately, walking very quickly, like people who are trying not to run. The screams are still audible. They come towards the camera.

DEBT COLLECTOR *off* : Murderers! Cut throats!

The camera follows the two men, then pans to reveal MME. HERMINE *and her* NEIGHBOUR *horrified and clinging to one another.*

MME. HERMINE *terrified* : Whatever is happening, Monsieur Forestier?

M. FORESTIER (*alias* LACENAIRE) : Nothing serious, Madame. Just some drunks fighting on the stairs, I'm going to call the police!

MONSIEUR FORESTIER *slips out, followed by* AVRIL. *The camera pans to follow their flight. Medium shot of the entrance to the staircase, shot slightly from below: the* DEBT COLLECTOR *appears, staggering, his clothes torn, head bare, face covered with blood, clutching his satchel to his bosom.*

DEBT COLLECTOR : Murderers! Murderers! . . . *Very close shot of his face.* Murderers!

It is daytime in the ' Boulevard du Temple '. *Medium shot of the crowd, which is very thick; then close medium shot of the doorway and the sign of* ' The Lion Cubs of the Temple '. *Backwards tracking shot to reveal* LACENAIRE *and* AVRIL *as they pass; the camera pans to follow them as they sit down facing one another at a table on the terrace, carefully choosing a place where they can see all the entrances and exits.* LACENAIRE, *breaking the silence, stares at* AVRIL, *and shakes his head.*

LACENAIRE : My poor Avril; you didn't make a very pleasing spectacle. You were as white as a ghost. *Lowering his voice.* And yet, you know, you weren't the victim!

Close shot of AVRIL, *three-quarters view, and* LACENAIRE *in profile — then a series of reverse angle shots.*

AVRIL *pathetic* : All the same, Monsieur Lacenaire, when I saw his head so close to mine, and his eyes!

LACENAIRE : If you'd hit him a bit quicker, you wouldn't have had time to notice his eyes!

[AVRIL *following his own ideas* : All the same, it's different at night, you can't see anything. But in the middle of the day like that, in the light, 'a human being' . . . it gives me a funny feeling!] (Not heard in the final versions.)

As LACENAIRE *shrugs his shoulders a* WAITER *comes up. The camera tracks slightly backwards to frame the group in medium shot.*

WAITER : What would you like, sir?

LACENAIRE : Something alcoholic . . . oh, anything you like!

AVRIL : Oh . . . A cup of hot chocolate, with cream.

LACENAIRE *smiles contemptuously. Cut.*

In MME. HERMINE'S *office, the same day. Close shot of a* POLICE CONSTABLE *in uniform, seen from the back, in the doorway. The camera pans to frame the doorway in a long shot.* MME. HERMINE *is sitting down on the left of the table. Behind the table, stretched out on a sofa is the* DEBT COLLECTOR, *his head wrapped in an impressive bandage. On the right of the table, standing up, is a* DETECTIVE *in civilian clothes, with a notebook in his hand.*

DEBT COLLECTOR *pouring himself brimming glasses of wine* : Like a lion, do you hear? Like a lion!

Another DETECTIVE *in civilian clothes appears, pacing backwards and forwards, he is the chief, the* INSPECTOR. *He looks careworn, and turns towards everyone in turn.*

INSPECTOR : A moment's silence, if you don't mind . . . *Pan towards* MME. HERMINE . . . You say, Madame, that this gentleman who called himself Monsieur Forestier, knew this Mademoiselle Garance. *She nods her head, the* INSPECTOR *turns towards the* DETECTIVE. Funny name, don't you think?

DEBT COLLECTOR *continuing to describe his exploit for his own ears*: I defended myself like a lion . . . *Raising his voice* . . . and I clung onto my satchel like a lioness . . . and they could hit me as much as they liked . . .

INSPECTOR *exasperated*: That's enough, if you don't mind.

DEBT COLLECTOR *not hearing*: That's right . . . my head's tough — I could take everything they handed out. *He pours himself another glass of wine and falls silent.*

   The INSPECTOR *paces up and down.*

INSPECTOR: You were saying, Madame?

MME. HERMINE: I don't know what I was saying. You can see, I'm quite distracted . . . Monsieur Forestier? Who ever would have thought that such a polite, well-bred man . . . and, another odd thing is that when I asked Mademoiselle Garance if she knew him, she replied, ' Monsieur Forestier? No, I don't know him.'

   [*Close shot of the* INSPECTOR *in the middle of the room.*

INSPECTOR: Of course, she didn't!

MME. HERMINE: At the time, it surprised me, I must say. *With a little smile.* There are some women who know so many people . . . discretion becomes second nature. *She smiles again.*] (Cut in the final version.)

   The same day, in an alleyway outside the ' Grand Relais '. Medium shot of a small crowd of idlers kept back by two policemen. People are trying to push past each other, and swap stories. General noise. The camera tracks forwards, and pans towards a few of them. (This little scene, like several other moments in the film is a conscious reminder of the beginning of an earlier film: ' Le Jour se Lève ', where the crowd mills around the hotel.)

FIRST LOUNGER *who knows what he is talking about*: Oh, yes, they threw him out of a third floor window. Isn't it dreadful? And he's the father of six children!

   The SECOND LOUNGER *turns his head to the right to pass on the news, the camera moves with him to reveal a* THIRD LOUNGER.

SECOND LOUNGER *to the other*: From the third floor! Did you hear that?

   A FOURTH *calls out to the* THIRD *who turns his head to the right — the camera follows him to reveal a* FOURTH LOUNGER.

FOURTH LOUNGER *to the* THIRD: Oh, I was told that he threw him-

120

self out of the window, and for the sake of a woman, into the bargain.

Outside in the ' Boulevard du Temple ' — the corner of the alleyway leading to the ' Grand Relais '. A crowd of curious people, attracted by the policeman and the first idlers, move slowly forward.

[FREDERICK *and* GARANCE, *arm in arm, come into shot from the right. The camera follows them and stops at the moment when* FREDERICK *stops, and gently holding* GARANCE *by both arms, pulls her towards him.*

FREDERICK : Really, Garance, is this serious? You want me to leave you alone?

GARANCE : Yes . . . I don't know why but I'm just — terribly sad ! It's stupid, but I want to cry. You know, it's like when you were little : you just threw yourself down on your bed and cried and cried. Didn't even know why — it's stupid ! But afterwards things are better.

FREDERICK : Well, if you want. *Smiling.* I'll come back when things are better. 'Bye, Garance.

GARANCE : 'Bye !

FREDERICK *turns and goes back the way they had come, and* GARANCE *starts down the alley. The camera follows her, and reveals the façade of the ' Grand Relais ' and the crowd outside.*] (This scene is in the script, but was never shot.)

Slightly high angle medium shot, using the crane and panning to follow GARANCE *through the crowd till she comes to the door. She asks as she passes by:*

GARANCE : What's happened?

AN IDLER *indignant* : It's a man who threw his wife out of the window. It's frightful — the mother of six children.

GARANCE *looks at him, rather amazed, and pushes through the crowd to the door. The camera pans to follow her; she stops in front of a* POLICEMAN.

POLICEMAN : You can't go in.

GARANCE : I live here.

POLICEMAN : Well, then, that's different.

He lets GARANCE *through.*

MME. HERMINE'S *office. Medium shot of the room and a view*

through the windows of the courtyard. GARANCE *can be seen as she passes on her way to the staircase which leads to the bedrooms.*

MME. HERMINE *noticing* GARANCE : Oh, there she is!

The INSPECTOR *jumps to the door, and calls.*

INSPECTOR : Mademoiselle?

The camera moves backwards rapidly and reveals the CONSTABLE *on guard at the door. It is the same one who tried to arrest* GARANCE, *at the beginning of the film.*

CONSTABLE *to the* INSPECTOR : But I know her!

INSPECTOR : That doesn't surprise me! *He calls again.* Mademoiselle!

Medium long shot of GARANCE *on the stairway. Surprised, she turns round.*

Cut back to the INSPECTOR *and the* CONSTABLE *standing on the threshold, in close shot.*

CONSTABLE : I've already arrested her once. It was an incident with a gold watch. I let her go, but it wasn't very clear.

INSPECTOR : Better and better.

GARANCE *reaches them. They go into the office. When she has crossed the threshold she stops and stares, astonished. The camera pans across the scene which greets her eyes:* MME. HERMINE *who is staring at her, the bandaged* DEBT COLLECTOR *lying on the sofa, the* DETECTIVE *giving her an unfriendly look.*

Medium long shot of the scene; the INSPECTOR *shuts the door and comes forward.*

INSPECTOR : I warn you, Mademoiselle, anything you say may be taken down and used in evidence against you.

GARANCE *unmoved* : Oh, well then, I won't say much!

INSPECTOR : We'll see about that. *He pushes forward a stool.* Sit down.

She sits in the centre of the room while the INSPECTOR *takes a chair and sits down astride it in front of her, and questions her.*

INSPECTOR *abruptly* : Well, what are you called?

GARANCE : I don't call myself; I'm always there. I don't need to call myself. But other people call me Garance, if you really want to know.

INSPECTOR : That's not a name !

GARANCE : It's the name of a flower. But my real name . . . *Smiling* . . . my maiden name, is Claire.

INSPECTOR : Claire what ?

GARANCE : Oh, Claire de lune . . . Claire . . .

Reverse angle shot of the INSPECTOR *full face and* GARANCE *three-quarters back view in the foreground. The* INSPECTOR *slowly gets up from his chair.*

INSPECTOR *furious* : Your surname, do you hear ?

*Reverse angle shot — * GARANCE *full face.*

GARANCE : My mother was called Reine. *Still calm and in no hurry.* Madame Reine. She didn't have any family. She was a foundling, as they say.

INSPECTOR *full face* : All right. What sort of work do you do ?

GARANCE *facing* : I'm an actress. *Pointing to* MME. HERMINE. I'm surprised Madame hasn't told you that already.

Close shot of MME. HERMINE, *silent and contemptuous. Then cut back to* GARANCE *and the* INSPECTOR *in profile.*

INSPECTOR *winking at his colleague out of shot* : Okay. Put ' Actress '.

Close shot of the DETECTIVE, *standing beside the wall. He writes it down with a question mark.*

DETECTIVE *under his breath* : Actress . . . in the bedroom !

Shot of the INSPECTOR *and* GARANCE *as seen by the* DETECTIVE. *Thus slightly shot from above.* GARANCE *turns round.*

GARANCE : Why are you being so rude to me ?

DETECTIVE : Oh . . . Oh . . .

INSPECTOR *facing* GARANCE : We're not being rude, we're joking. And where are you an actress, Mademoiselle ? And since when ?

GARANCE : At the ' Funambules '. Since about three weeks ago.

INSPECTOR *to the* DETECTIVE : A bird of passage ? . . . *To* GARANCE . . . And before the ' Funambules ', what did you do ?

Medium close-up of GARANGE *full face, the* INSPECTOR *half out of shot. Then a series of reverse angle shots following the dialogue.*

GARANCE : I used to pose for painters.

INSPECTOR : That's easy to say ! *Abruptly.* What painters ? Where ?

GARANCE : For all sorts of people — Monsieur Ingres, for example.

INSPECTOR : Monsieur Ingres ? . . . Never heard of him.

GARANCE : I'm surprised, I'd have thought he was rather up your street.

INSPECTOR : Eh?

GARANCE : Yes. In his spare moments, he plays the fiddle.

INSPECTOR *furious* : Look here, you little . . . That sort of joke . . .

GARANCE *interrupting* : You make jokes yourself.

Medium long shot of the room, the INSPECTOR *addresses himself more to his colleague than to* GARANCE, *who is out of shot.*

INSPECTOR : I suppose it's useless to ask ' Mademoiselle ' in what costume she posed for painters?

Slight pan to frame, in the background, the old DEBT COLLECTOR, *who sits up. Almost a general shot, with* GARANCE *half out of shot on the right.*

DEBT COLLECTOR : A lovely girl like that ! . . . What a question ! I ask you, what's painting for, anyway?

INSPECTOR *interrupting* : Would you mind leaving me alone to get on with my enquiry?

DEBT COLLECTOR : Your enquiry ! Your enquiry's all over, because I'm safe and sound after all ! *He drinks and leans back again.*

The INSPECTOR *has got up.* GARANCE *turns round towards the* DEBT COLLECTOR.

GARANCE *pointing* : Is this the man who threw his wife out of the window? *Cut to a close-up of the* DEBT COLLECTOR *who smiles at* GARANCE. I don't believe it. He looks like a very nice man.

Medium shot of GARANCE *and the* INSPECTOR. *The latter shakes his chair in a rage.*

INSPECTOR *very unpleasant* : All right, that's enough of that !

GARANCE *suddenly fed up* : What's all this about, anyway? What have I done? I don't understand anything that's going on.

INSPECTOR : We'll make you understand. *He walks round her as he talks.* First, you're going to tell us, very nicely, just who Monsieur Forestier is.

GARANCE *pointing to* MME. HERMINE : Madame already asked me that. I don't know any Monsieur Forestier.

Close shot of MME. HERMINE, *the* DEBT COLLECTOR *in the background.*

MME. HERMINE : Oh ! . . . just listen to her !

The camera pans to frame GARANCE *again, sitting down facing the camera. The* INSPECTOR, *standing close to her,*

leans down and peers into her face.
INSPECTOR : Of course . . . but maybe you know him under another name.

He takes from behind him the report his colleague is holding. The camera pans to follow the movement of his hand.
INSPECTOR *reading* : ' A young man, dressed in black, with carefully manicured hands. He expresses himself elegantly, and always wears a well-starched shirt front.' *He gives back the report, and starts walking round* GARANCE *again.* Does that mean anything to you, that description? . . . The starched shirt?
GARANCE : Oh, me, you know I used to be a laundress, so starched linen . . .
INSPECTOR : Yet another profession. *Ironic.* At least that one is respectable.
GARANCE : Respectable . . . yes. And it would even be a very pleasant occupation . . . *She looks at the* INSPECTOR, *whose linen is rather grubby* . . . if people were cleaner.
Medium shot of GARANCE *back view, the* INSPECTOR *and the* POLICE CONSTABLE *at the door.*
CONSTABLE *approaching as the* INSPECTOR *gives him a sign* : Yes, chief. I've seen this man, and he was with her. *To* GARANCE. That's right, I saw you both together, the day you stole the watch.
GARANCE *choking with indignation* : Oh !
INSPECTOR : Well, well, Mademoiselle works with watches as well.
GARANCE *close-up of her, full face. She speaks to the* POLICE CONSTABLE *who is out of shot* : But look here, you know very well that it wasn't me, because you let me go.
CONSTABLE *close shot* : And believe me, I regretted it. *The camera pulls back, he speaks to the* INSPECTOR. If it wasn't her, it was him, and since they were together, there can't be any mistake about it.
Medium close-up of GARANCE *beginning to get worried. Reverse angle shot; the* INSPECTOR *pulls the* POLICE CONSTABLE *to one side; the camera makes a slight pan to follow them. Then the* INSPECTOR *turns back to talk to* GARANCE; *he is facing the camera, she is backview, in the foreground.*
INSPECTOR *with sudden, hypocritical familiarity* : Come on, don't make a face like that. It's nothing, this business with the watch. Just a trifle, we won't mention it again. *Medium close-up of* GARANCE; *he continues, off.* A little hors-d'œuvre. — Now let's talk of

the main dish: attempted murder, with premeditation. *General shot. He points at her with his finger.* Aiding and abetting. That could put you away for five or six years . . . at least! *More and more familiar.* So you see what I mean. What we're telling you is for your own good. We're being nice, friendly. We're laying the table. Let's sit down and begin.

> *Medium shot of both of them; the* INSPECTOR *puts a ' friendly ' hand on her shoulder. She is facing the camera, he is backview in the foreground.*

INSPECTOR : We'll take it into account.

GARANCE *abruptly, pulling herself away* : Leave me alone. Don't touch me.

INSPECTOR *wounded* : Oh, she has scruples, does she?

GARANCE *calm once more* : Why not? I'm innocent.

INSPECTOR *getting annoyed* : Oh, we've heard enough of that!

> *Medium long shot; he takes her by the arm and forces her to get up.*

INSPECTOR *to his colleagues*: Okay. We're not going to discuss it any longer. We're taking her along. She can talk down at the station.

GARANCE *pulling herself free again* : Taking her away, are you? Now wait a minute. You'd better watch out . . . Fragile. Precious object. Handle with care. I'm afraid you don't know who you're dealing with.

> *Medium close-up of* MME. HERMINE, *sceptical. Medium close-up of the* DEBT COLLECTOR, *enjoying himself, immensely; close shot of the* POLICE CONSTABLE, *frowning; close shot of the* INSPECTOR *and of* GARANCE. *The latter is holding out a visiting card which she has taken out of her bag.*

GARANCE : Would you be kind enough to let this person know that I am the victim of a judicial error?

> *The* INSPECTOR, *very uneasy, takes the card. He reads it, and his face expresses astonishment. Medium close-up of* GARANCE, *ironic. Long shot:* GARANCE *is standing in the centre of the room. Music. The curtain falls. A title comes up.*

END OF PART ONE

(Sometimes there is an interval here, and sometimes it
is shown as two separate films.)

CHILDREN
OF PARADISE

Part Two

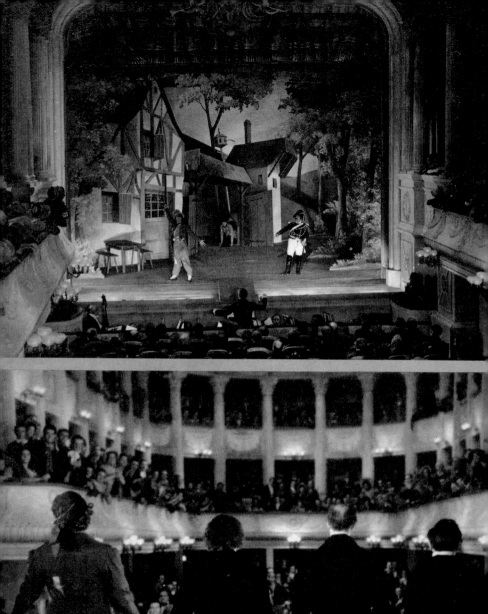

PART TWO
THE MAN IN WHITE

A luxurious theatre curtain. The footlights come on and the three knocks which signal the beginning of the performance are heard off. The credit titles are shown again. Background music is a romantic waltz. After the credits the title: PART II — THE MAN IN WHITE.
A series of cards are shown on the screen, describing the story so far.

CARD A : The famous mime Baptiste Debureau is passionately in love with a young actress named Garance. Out of shyness, Baptiste misses his opportunity to win Garance, and she becomes the mistress of the well-known actor, Frederick Lemaître.

CARD B : At the little theatre of the ' Funambules ' where they are all three playing, a rich dandy of the period, Count Edward de Monteray, introduces himself to Garance and offers her his protection.

CARD C : She refuses at first, but when falsely accused of aiding and abetting an attempted murder, plotted by her friend Lacenaire, Garance, to prove her innocence, holds out to the astonished policeman, the Count's card.

(Cut from versions where the film is shown in its entirety.)

LAST CARD : Several years have passed
The curtain. The three knocks are repeated. The background music ends and is replaced by general bustle of the street and atmosphere noises as the curtain rises.
Long shot of the street.
It is daytime on the ' Boulevard du Temple ', which presents its usual animated week-day bustle. The theatres are closed. There are not many performers, but a lot of people walking, particularly workmen, children and tradesmen. Carriages and cabs

133

pass each other in the street. The camera pans to follow a carriage which passes in front of it. FREDERICK LEMAITRE *can be recognised inside, smiling, confident, happier than ever to be alive, and dressed very elegantly. There is a very pretty girl on his right, another on his left. Close shot of the trio sitting in the carriage facing the camera. In the background the street can be seen passing by.*

FREDERICK : The worst play anyone has ever dared to produce, even on the ' Street of Many Murders.' The worst, absolutely the worst.

FIRST PRETTY GIRL : Why are you acting in it, then?

FREDERICK : Because I signed a contract.

SECOND PRETTY GIRL : Why did you sign it?

FREDERICK : I needed the money !

FIRST PRETTY GIRL : But you earn fantastic sums of money !

FREDERICK: A man like me never has any, because he always spends more.

Medium long shot of the Boulevard; the camera follows the carriage in a semi-circular pan until it comes to a stop in front of the ' Grand Theatre '. *Medium shot as the camera tracks slightly backwards and* FREDERICK *gets down. A* STAGE DOOR-KEEPER *runs up and as he helps the* PRETTY GIRLS *get down, speaks to* FREDERICK.

STAGE DOORKEEPER : They're waiting for you ! . . . The authors are getting impatient.

A few passers-by press round FREDERICK, *who raises his arms to push them aside.*

FREDERICK : Some air . . . let's have some air !

[*A group approaches the carriage. Some of the women recognise* FREDERICK.

A YOUNG WOMAN : Oh ! . . . Frederick Lemaître !

A MAN *shrugging his shoulders* : So what? . . . he's just a man like anyone else !

YOUNG WOMAN *to the* MAN : Well, he certainly isn't like you ! *She waves, and murmurs in adoration.* Oh, Frederick !

FIRST PRETTY GIRL *blushing* : Oh ! . . . they've recognised us !]
(Shot, but cut in the final editing.)

The camera pans to follow the two girls towards the door of the theatre that FREDERICK *has hired. The pan continues, and stops on a poster on the doorway.*

134

GRAND THEATRE
A New Season of
FREDERICK LEMAITRE
in
BRIGANDS INN*
Melodrama by Anthieu, Saint-Amand and
Polygathe

(In the original script, the author's names were carefully made illegible. They were, in fact, intended to represent Benjamin Antier, Saint-Amand and Paulyanthe, minor authors only known through their connection with the historical character of Lemaître.)

A streamer is pasted diagonally across the poster. It reads, in very large letters:

IN REHEARSAL

The camera pans again to reveal the STAGE DOORKEEPER *running after* FREDERICK.

STAGE DOORKEEPER : Hurry up, Monsieur Frederick . . . They're waiting for you.

Long shot of the auditorium of the 'Grand Theatre'. *In the background the stage is empty and unfurnished. In the auditorium itself, lit only by the footlights, two men are seated respectively in the first and second rows of the stalls; two others, standing, pace nervously to and fro between the third and fourth rows of seats. The man in the first row is jovial and good-natured; he is the* DIRECTOR *of the theatre, and he watches the three others: serious, dressed in dark suits and all in very bad tempers, with the calm eye and placid smile of someone who has seen and heard it all before.*

Medium long shot of the auditorium seen from the stage. The FIRST AUTHOR *takes out his watch.*

FIRST AUTHOR : If it's true that punctuality is . . .

The two other authors stop and complete the phrase at the same time as the first.

SECOND AND THIRD AUTHORS *in chorus with the* FIRST : . . . is the politeness of kings.

---

* Translator's Note : The French title of FREDERICK's play was ' L'Auberge des Adrets '. The ' Adrets ' were a notorious family of brigands.

135

First Author *ending his sentence* : . . . it certainly isn't that of Frederick Lemaître!

As the Director *raises his arms to heaven as a sign of his powerlessness, the two other* Authors *reply.*

Second and Third Authors : Indeed it is not!

In Frederick's *dressing room, which is very big and gloriously untidy; a curtain divides the room into two parts, one furnished like a small reception room, and the other is where* Frederick *dresses and makes-up. On the walls are signed portraits, and also portraits of* Frederick *in his 'greatest roles'. On a table a bottle of champagne waits in a bucket, and there is also a large bowl of mulled wine. Medium shot of the curtain behind which* Frederick *is getting dressed.*

Frederick *off — apparently in the height of indignation* : And they call themselves 'literary gentlemen' . . . *heavy emphasis on 'gentlemen'* . . . Really, sometimes I wonder why perfectly respectable people . . . *heavy emphasis on respectable* . . . should spend all their time writing stories about brigands!

The camera tracks backwards and pans in a circle at the same time to show the whole room. The Two Pretty Girls *are standing by the table. Suddenly a hand, then an arm appear round the curtain.*

Frederick : Let's have something to drink, my little kittens . . . for pity's sake let's have something to drink! (*Still on page 129*)

The Two Pretty Girls *race to obey him, and one laughingly fills a glass with the mulled wine and hands it to* Frederick, *while the other watches her, cross and disappointed.*

Close shot of Frederick *who appears facing the camera, fully made-up, with a hat on his head. He is dressed as* Robert Macaire, *the hero of the play, his costume is not new, but it is still presentable. He goes to sit down in front of the dressing table and takes the proffered glass.*

Frederick *looking at himself in the mirror* : Of course, it's not very good. Poor Robert Macaire! . . . *he drinks*. Well my little kittens? What's happening, I don't hear you any more . . . hm . . .

Medium long shot of the room favouring the Two Girls, *one is sitting down and sulking, and the other is standing close by her.*

First Girl *sitting* : We're unhappy.

136

SECOND GIRL : Yes, you see both of us love you, but we're good friends, so . . .

FREDERICK *off* : So? . . .

FIRST GIRL : We don't want to fall out with each other and we don't know what to do.

The camera pans to frame FREDERICK *who walks towards them as he speaks, and then the camera pans in the opposite direction to frame the girls with him. At the end of his speech he pours himself a new glass of wine from the ladle in the bowl.*

FREDERICK : What do you mean you don't know what to do? *Smiling.* Do what I do, act, since you want to be actresses. When I act, I am desperately in love, desperately, do you understand? . . . But when the curtain falls, the audience goes away, and takes ' my love ' with it.

He smiles broadly, and continues to drink, then he goes over to lean against the mantelpiece, and stare curiously at his glass. Medium shot of FREDERICK.

FREDERICK : You see, I make the audience a present of my love. The audience is very happy, and so am I. And I become wise and free and calm and sensible, again, like Baptiste! *Suddenly enraged.* There I am, I go and do it again!

He is very upset, straightens up, and then frustrated, throws his glass to the ground with a melodramatic gesture and a noise of breaking glass.

FREDERICK : I can't stand it! You never hear anything else : ' Baptiste, have you seen Baptiste! ' A real bore . . . Even Théophile Gautier has to put his oar in : ' Go and see Baptiste! Go and see " Rag and Bone Man " '! A masterpiece.'

(It was absolutely true that Théophile Gautier had many times praised the mime Jean-Gaspard Deburau, especially in ' Pierrot in Africa ', ' The Trials ', ' Black and White '. As for the ' Brigands Inn ', Gautier mentioned the two actors who played the principal roles, (one of which was Lemaître as Macaire) but joked about the play. Of the characters, Macaire and his accomplice Bertrand, he wrote ironically that they were ' the Orestes and Pylades of the convict world.' 1823.)

He shrugs his shoulders, in irritation, and returns to the Two

PRETTY GIRLS. *The camera pans to follow him.*

FREDERICK *contemptuous*: A masterpiece! A pantomime! He exaggerates, Théophile!

> *Suddenly he notices that the* FIRST PRETTY GIRL, *shot of her near the wall decorated with photographs, is playing with Phoebe's crescent that is hanging on the wall, the crescent moon that* GARANCE *wore in her hair at the* ' Funambules '.

FREDERICK *off*: Don't touch that! . . . That's a memory; it hurts.
> *He comes over to her; medium shot of all three of them, and takes the crescent out of her hands.*

FREDERICK *emphatically*: The snake of memory! The sting of regret! The red light of forgetfulness! . . . *He bursts out laughing.* Foolishness, dreams, air! *He turns round again and looks the* FIRST PRETTY GIRL *up and down.* What I like is reality. *He gives the* FIRST PRETTY GIRL *a resounding smack on the bottom and caresses her.* Lovely! . . . a fine piece of work . . . Two acts, but solidly constructed . . . My compliments to the authors!

FIRST PRETTY GIRL *pulling herself away, outraged*: Really, how can you be so vulgar!

> *The other* PRETTY GIRL, *sitting down, bursts out laughing while the camera pans to follow the first one, who angrily picks up her bag and walks in front of* FREDERICK *who is also smiling.*

FIRST PRETTY GIRL *to her friend*: Oh! And you think it's funny? . . . I'm not in the least surprised that you like that sort of thing! Well, I certainly don't. *She prepares to leave.* Not me, thank you very much. Not me!

> *She goes out, banging the door behind her. The camera has moved back to the other girl who has stood up and gone over to* FREDERICK. *(None of the scripts mention this departure. In fact, the two girls stay quietly there until* CELESTIN *arrives. So, even the beginning of the scene must have been improvised in front of the cameras.)*

SECOND PRETTY GIRL: There we are . . . alone at last!

> FREDERICK *embraces her.*

FREDERICK: Are you angry with me?

PRETTY GIRL *all smiles*: Oh . . . no!

> *They kiss passionately.*
> *The camera tracks backwards and pans to frame the door of*

the dressing room. Someone knocks. No reply. They knock again nervously. No reply. The door opens. A young actor appears, wearing the costume of BERTRAND, MACAIRE'S *accomplice. The camera pans to follow him right up to the couple who have their arms round each other, and are still kissing.*

CELESTIN : Oh . . . I'm sorry !

FREDERICK *drags his lips away from the* YOUNG GIRL'S *for an instant.*

FREDERICK : What's the matter, Célestin?

CELESTIN *is a bit embarrassed in front of this couple embracing so passionately.*

CELESTIN : Oh, er . . . nothing, er, I mean I just wanted to warn you, that they are waiting for you.

(End of the improvisation.)

FREDERICK *starting*: Oh ! . . . *upset* . . . Poor authors ! *He smiles. He pulls himself away from the* PRETTY GIRL. *Close shot of all three.*

CELESTIN : Oh, no, no, no. I'm not talking about the authors. The authors started rehearsing without us a long time ago.

FREDERICK *winking* : Then it must be some admirers?

CELESTIN *also winking* : That's right . . . admirers.

FREDERICK : I come ! . . . *Taking the* PRETTY GIRL *by the chin.* I'll be back soon, my sweetheart. Try to tidy everything up . . . when you've finished looking around. Then, when I come back everything will be perfect.

FREDERICK *and* CELESTIN *come out of the dressing room and walk down the corridor towards the camera, which precedes them, tracking backwards, talking as they go.*

FREDERICK : Your costume's terrible, Célestin . . . As bad as mine. No imagination, as dull as ditchwater !

A STAGE MANAGER *comes on from the left, in a state of hysterical fury.*

STAGE MANAGER : The director is asking for you, gentlemen. Please ! this is intolerable !

FREDERICK *very dignified* : We are coming, my friend. (*Still on page 129*)

The STAGE MANAGER, *vaguely reassured, goes out right.* FREDERICK *takes a few more steps, followed by the camera.*

FREDERICK : Let's have a look at these rascals!

He leans down over the bannister of the staircase. Tilt down on the four or five 'admirers' as seen by FREDERICK, *as they talk animatedly on the floor below. These are all very well-dressed gentlemen, who, as they wait for* FREDERICK *are arguing, plotting and showing signs of angry impatience. They are talking very quietly, heads bent, in a circle, so that they cannot be recognised. Return on* FREDERICK *who stands up and smiles at* CELESTIN. *Medium shot of the two,* FREDERICK *in the foreground.*

FREDERICK : Yes, I get the gist of it. Jealous husbands, anxious creditors, abandoned lovers! . . .

CELESTIN : Yes, as usual!

FREDERICK : Embittered people, unhappy people . . . rubbish.

CELESTIN : So?

FREDERICK : Well . . . so what? *Making the best of it.* You go ahead, and I'll plunge into the rubbish-bin . . . as usual!

They come down the stairs quickly. CELESTIN *in front, high angle shot, very dignified. Medium long shot of the floor below. The men wait, furious and threatening at the bottom of the stairs.* CELESTIN *plunges in among them without too much trouble,* FREDERICK *is set upon immediately.*

FREDERICK *very dignified* : Come on, now . . . Gentlemen.

He tries to escape, but they all join in.

THE MEN : Corruptor of innocence! . . . My money! . . . What about my bills! . . . Mountebank, satyr, lousy gypsy!

Blows begin to rain down on FREDERICK'S *head, and he hits back. General mêlée.*

FREDERICK *calling* : Help! Bertrand! . . . They're killing Robert Macaire! Help, Cossacks! They're beating Frederick the Great!

CELESTIN, *with a cudgel, throws himself into the fight and hits whoever he can reach.*

MEN IN THE SCUFFLE : A woman from one of the best families, you ought to be ashamed! Bandit, rascal! I've never seen anything like it! Come on, beat him up!

Meanwhile in the auditorium, a general shot from the back of the stage shows, in contrast to the tumult of the previous scene, an impressive calm. Reverse angle shot of the stage, bare of scenery, where two artistes rehearse in absolute silence,

very seriously, and with complete conviction. There is an OLD
WOMAN (MARIE), *poorly dressed, with realistic make-up which
makes her features look drawn, and a* NON-COMMISSIONED
OFFICER. *The woman is talking to the* AUTHORS *who are sitting in the stalls.*

MARIE : If I've understood correctly, when I hear the shot I come
out of the Inn?

*Reverse angle shot of the auditorium from her point of view,
slightly high angle.*

FIRST AUTHOR : Yes, and you throw yourself onto the body.

SECOND AUTHOR : Or rather onto the place where the body ought
to be, since we are still waiting for Monsieur Lemaître.

Reverse angle shot of the stage from the AUTHORS *point of
view, slightly shot from below.*

NON-COMMISSIONED OFFICER *to the* AUTHORS : Right you are. *To*
MARIE. All right, let's go!

MARIE *returns to the back of the stage, and waits for her
partner to give her the cue.*

*Seeing that she is ready, he begins to rehearse, addressing
himself to an imaginary person in front of him.*

NON-COMMISSIONED OFFICER : The hour of justice has sounded.
You will not escape punishment.

He aims point blank and fires.

NON-COMMISSIONED OFFICER : Pow! . . .

At the ' shot ', MARIE *mimes the gestures of a hysterical woman
who throws open an imaginary door and throws herself onto
the stage in the place where the corpse should have been.*

MARIE : Alas, you have killed him! Oh wretched life! He was a
wicked man, but he was my husband!

Reverse angle shot of the THREE AUTHORS *and the* DIRECTOR.

FIRST AUTHOR *standing up* : Bravo! . . .

The THREE AUTHORS *look at each other.*

FIRST AUTHOR : Forgive me, I was carried away by the drama. All
the same I should like, if it were possible, a little bit more . . . a bit
more . . .

THE THREE *together* : A bit more feeling.

*Reverse angle shot: the stage in medium long shot. At that
moment, a voice can be heard coming from the wings.*

FREDERICK *off* : That's it, more feeling. *He laughs.*

141

Then FREDERICK *makes his entrance, with* BERTRAND *beside him.* FREDERICK'S *costume is in tatters, his shirt torn and crumpled, his hat bashed in. Over his right eye he is wearing a huge black scarf.*

FREDERICK : Feeling, more feeling, and always feeling! *He sniggers. Reverse angle shot of the* AUTHORS *in close shot: they leap up simultaneously.*

Reverse angle shot of FREDERICK, *beaming as he addresses himself to the* AUTHORS.

FREDERICK : Dare I hope, gentlemen, that the costume meets with your approval?

Reverse angle shot: the DIRECTOR *and then the* AUTHORS, *in one panning shot.*

DIRECTOR : Not bad, it's original!

He turns towards the AUTHORS. *The camera pans to reveal them.*

FIRST AUTHOR *choking with indignation* : It's not possible . . . it's a . . .

SECOND AND THIRD AUTHORS : It's a practical joke!

Reverse angle: low angle, medium shot of FREDERICK *raising his arms to heaven, then a series of identical reverse angle shots according to the dialogue.*

FREDERICK : Don't forget, gentlemen, that Robert Macaire . . . *Gesturing towards* BERTRAND, *cut to* BERTRAND . . . and his odious accomplice, have not just come from their tailor's, but from the prison at Toulon. They are bandits, not dandies.

FIRST AUTHOR *overwhelmed* : All the same, that black bandage!

SECOND AUTHOR : It's horrible to look at!

FREDERICK *smiling* : Perhaps, but the eye underneath it is even more horrible! *He shows his eye, which is black and swollen.*

DIRECTOR *exasperated* : Please, gentlemen, don't let's have another fight, I beg of you!

He points to the actress who is playing the part of MARIE.

DIRECTOR : Since Frederick's here let's rehearse the scene with the two of them, scene eleven, all right?

FREDERICK : I'd rather do the scene with the policemen, I find it more amusing.

FIRST AUTHOR *very pompous and annoyed* : We are not here,

gentlemen, to ' make the whole world laugh '.

Long shot of the stage from the point of view of the AUTHORS *and the* DIRECTOR.

FREDERICK : What a pity. *Sighing.* Ah, well, if you insist. *To the* ACTRESS. Let's start then, Latour . . . scene eleven.

Long shot: the stage, with the auditorium in the background, and the actors in the foreground. MARIE *advances, ' facing the audience '.*

MARIE *pathetic* : Oh ! My son, you are the only thing which gives me courage to bear the sight of him, he who has been the author of all our misfortunes !

ROBERT MACAIRE (FREDERICK) : Heavens ! My wife !

He tries to escape, but she advances on him. Medium long shot of the stage as seen by the AUTHORS.

MARIE : Yes, your wife, your victim, Marie . . . the wretched Marie !

ROBERT MACAIRE *stopping and gesturing towards her as he speaks to the* AUTHORS : It's true, she's not very gay.

FIRST AUTHOR *quick close shot* : Oh, please, spare us your comments.

Cut back to the stage in medium long shot.

ROBERT MACAIRE : Come on, Marie, take your cue. *In the part, very theatrical* . . . I am discovered ! *To* MARIE . . . And it is you, Marie, who has denounced me ?

MARIE *painfully exasperated* : Yes, to save my son !

ROBERT MACAIRE : To save your son you have betrayed his father.

MARIE *more and more exasperated* : Alas !

ROBERT MACAIRE *aside* : Pretend to be moved ! *To* MARIE. Marie, my poor Marie !

MARIE *moved* : Robert . . . my poor Robert ! Is it possible that you have committed so many crimes !

ROBERT MACAIRE *aside* : What do you expect, Marie, everyone has their little weaknesses !

Astonishment of MARIE *at this departure from the text, and quick shot of the* AUTHORS *who have sat bolt upright in their seats like one man.*

THE AUTHORS *outraged* : Stop ! That reply was not in the text.

FREDERICK *alias* MACAIRE : Since there's absolutely nothing in your play, it's got to be padded out a little.

Quick shot of the AUTHORS.

AUTHORS : Oh! We won't stand for this!

Medium shot of FREDERICK *between his two fellow actors. Beside himself, he strides about the stage, then advances towards the footlights; the camera follows him tracking and panning.*

FREDERICK : Exactly. Your wretched ' Inn ' is empty, empty . . . *With a guffaw of laughter* . . . I suppose you expect the audience to bring their dinner with them. Apples. Perhaps they'll bring some tomatoes too! And you call this a drama. Poor drama, and three acts of it into the bargain. *Looking at the* AUTHORS. One act for each of you, so that nobody need be jealous! Three acts. *Chuckling.* I call it three evil actions! *

FIRST AUTHOR *shot of the trio* : Please don't play on words!

FREDERICK *camera on him* : What do you want me to play with? Your ideas? You don't have any.

Medium long shot, slightly high angle, of the DIRECTOR *and the* AUTHORS *in the auditorium, as seen by* FREDERICK, *followed by a series of reverse angle shots.*

DIRECTOR : Look here, Frederick!

FIRST AUTHOR *putting on an air of contemptuous calmness:* Nothing can surprise us . . . nothing can wound us coming from someone who started his career at the ' Funambules '.

THE THREE AUTHORS *together* : Walking on his hands.

FREDERICK *smiling* : And why not on my hands? You've certainly managed to write a play with your feet!

SECOND AUTHOR *trembling* : Monsieur!

The FIRST AUTHOR *gestures haughtily to the others to allow him to deal with this.*

FIRST AUTHOR : You force us . . . I am afraid, to play our final card. *Pompous and sententious* . . . Monsieur, you have signed a contract, you have received . . .

FREDERICK *medium low angle shot* : . . . and spent . . .

THE AUTHORS *in chorus* : . . . a pretty sum!

FIRST AUTHOR *waving to the others to be quiet* : Are you prepared to honour your obligations? Are you prepared to act in our play?

---

*Translator's Note: The pun (not a very good one) is on the French word ' acte ', which means both Act of a play and deed.

FREDERICK : Of course, gentlemen, on condition that it allows itself to be acted ! . . .

After a rapid wipe, the auditorium of the same theatre in general shot on the opening night of the ' BRIGANDS INN '. Seen from the stage, in long shot, the auditorium is packed and the spectators are laughing and applauding fit to split their sides. Reverse angle shot of the stage, seen from the back of the auditorium. ROBERT MACAIRE *and the* NON-COMMIS-SIONED OFFICER *are face to face, on the centre of the stage; nearby the* PROMPTER *in his hole, out of shot, in the middle of the footlights.*

NON-COMMISSIONED OFFICER : Enough. We have a description of the guilty ones, do not try to flee. All the ways of escape are guarded. . . . one of them is called Rémond. *Medium shot of the two of them.* But we know his real name — this man is called Robert Macaire . . . *Raising his voice for dramatic effect* . . . and Robert Macaire . . .

But before he can finish his sentence ROBERT MACAIRE *points a finger at him and says:*

ROBERT MACAIRE : Is you !

The actor is dumbfounded.

Laughter in the audience.

FREDERICK *thoroughly enjoying himself* : And prove me the contrary if you can! *He comes up to the footlights and addresses the audience.* What can he reply, since it isn't in the script . . . and while he tries to think of a suitable come-back, I've got a chance to escape again.

General laughter again. Medium close-up of the face of the old PROMPTER, *flabbergasted. Quick close shot of the three* AUTHORS *sitting in a stage box, very uneasy. Long shots and quick medium shots of the laughing audience. Cut back to the stage seen in long shot.*

MACAIRE *moves towards the other side. From behind,* BERT-RAND (CELESTIN) *peers out of a dog kennel.*

MACAIRE : Come on, Médor, let's get going! The old play's still got a bit of life in it ! (*Still on page 130*)

He whistles, like one would whistle for a dog, and BERTRAND *emerges from his kennel and starts off in his master's footsteps.*

BERTRAND : Okay, guv, I'm coming.

He trots out on all fours, gets up with great dignity, and follows FREDERICK *into the wings. Shot of the* CONDUCTOR, *not knowing what to do, but automatically waving his baton. Shot of the horrified* AUTHORS *who cower in their box, then cut back to the stage where the* NON-COMMISSIONED OFFICER *stands like a statue, his arms still raised to heaven.*

NON-COMMISSIONED OFFICER: Frederick, please, come back! Come back, I beg you!

General shot of the audience roaring with laughter. Cut to the CONDUCTOR *who continues to beat time. Cut to the* AUTHORS *who gaze at each other, stupefied with horror. Behind them can be seen the* DIRECTOR, *in raptures.*
Cut back to the stage in long shot.

NON-COMMISSIONED OFFICER *even more desperate*: Hey, Frederick! . . . Frederick! . . .

Medium shot of a stage box on the courtyard side opposite the one occupied by the AUTHORS. *It is occupied by a couple.* ROBERT MACAIRE, *followed by* BERTRAND, *enters; the couple withdraw.* MACAIRE *sits down quite calmly.*
Cut back to a general shot of the stage; the NON-COMMISSIONED OFFICER *stands, looking more and more stupid, in the centre of the stage. Suddenly he remembers one of his earlier lines, and shouts blindly in the direction of the wings:*

NON-COMMISSIONED OFFICER: Arrest him! Arrest them! Or it is possible they will escape us once more.

Quick cut to the audience who are laughing and applauding for all they are worth. Quick cut to the AUTHORS *perplexed and very uneasy at this applause.*
Medium shot, slightly high angle, of the stage boxes, where FREDERICK *is applauding very loudly and shouting:*

FREDERICK: Bravo! Bravo! Bravo!

Pan to frame the stage with FREDERICK'S *box in the picture. The* NON-COMMISSIONED OFFICER *turns round and comes right down to the footlights, facing* FREDERICK.

NON-COMMISSIONED OFFICER: Do not try to flee, you are surrounded!

ROBERT MACAIRE *inviting the audience to be his witnesses*: Oh, please my friend, can't I even go to the theatre?

146

The NON-COMMISSIONED OFFICER *hesitates and the audience laughs.*

NON-COMMISSIONED OFFICER : Enough talk. You are mine !

ROBERT MACAIRE : You naughty man !

NON-COMMISSIONED OFFICER *more and more embarrassed* : Well, I mean . . . er . . . you are unmasked ! You are Robert Macaire !

ROBERT MACAIRE *with calm assurance* : No, no, certainly not.

> *The* NON-COMMISSIONED OFFICER *full face and* ROBERT MACAIRE *and* BERTRAND, *backview in the foreground. The* NON-COMMISSIONED OFFICER *suddenly looks cunning and sure of himself.*

NON-COMMISSIONED OFFICER *quickly, triumphantly* : Since you deny being Robert Macaire, escaped from Toulon prison, reply quickly and without hesitation to this question . . . who are you ?

> *High angle shot of* BERTRAND *and* MACAIRE *facing the camera, the* NON-COMMISSIONED OFFICER *in the foreground, three-quarter back view, and half out of the picture.*

MACAIRE *standing up majestically* : I am Frederick Lemaître !

> *Quick cuts of the general hilarity among the audience, then medium shot of the three* AUTHORS *nearly bursting with rage and embarrassment. Cut back to high angle shot of* MACAIRE *and* BERTRAND, *with the* NON-COMMISSIONED OFFICER *in the foreground, then the camera tracks slightly backwards to frame them in mid shot.*

NON-COMMISSIONED OFFICER : I've had enough of this, I arrest you !

MACAIRE *to the audience* : Oh, he's off again. *To* BERTRAND. What shall we do with him ? Shall we kill him ?

BERTRAND : Kill a policeman ? . . . well, there's no harm in wishing.

> MACAIRE *pulls out his revolver and aims at the* NON-COMMISSIONED OFFICER *who draws back. A shot rings out.*
>
> *Quick shot backstage, the interior of the ' house '.* MARIE, *who has been standing behind a piece of scenery painted to represent the door of her cottage, dreaming, jumps when she hears this signal and tries to open the door, which leads on stage. The door will not open.*
>
> *The stage seen from the audience. The* NON-COMMISSIONED OFFICER, *after the shot, stands dumb-struck.*

MACAIRE : Fall down, stupid, you're dead !

Quick cut to MARIE *who is banging on the door that she cannot open.*

On stage, the NON-COMMISSIONED OFFICER, *automatically obeying* MACAIRE, *collapses at the moment when* MARIE *finally succeeds in opening the door and making her entrance. She throws herself towards the body without looking to see who it is.*

MARIE *kneeling before the body* : You have killed him, oh, wretched life ! He was a wicked man, but he was my husband !

Medium shot of the box, slightly high angle.

MACAIRE : Be comforted, my widow, it was a false alarm.

Medium shot of MARIE, *leaning over the corpse of the* NON-COMMISSIONED OFFICER *and suddenly realising her mistake. She does not know what to do. Cut back to* MACAIRE, *grandiloquent.*

MACAIRE : You can dry your tears. Your little husband is alive.

Cut back to MARIE *and the* NON-COMMISSIONED OFFICER. *He gets up onto one elbow, pushing* MARIE *roughly aside.*

NON-COMMISSIONED OFFICER *in a sepulchral voice* : Not for long !

He pulls out his revolver and shoots at FREDERICK. *Medium shot of* MACAIRE/FREDERICK *in his box, who immediately puts his hand to his heart, and to stop himself from falling, clings on to the edge of the box.*

MACAIRE : Ah ! . . . it had to finish like this !

It is his turn to collapse over the edge of the box, and then raising his head slightly, to gaze at MARIE. BERTRAND *supports him. Medium shot while he is speaking, then close shot.*

MACAIRE : I die. Farewell, Marie ! And forgive me ! No, I was not a bad man. But I got led into bad habits. Mine was only the arm which carries out orders, the hand which strikes, the foot which leaves its tracks in the dust of crime . . . *Regaining a little strength before he dies* . . . But the real criminals, the ones who plotted everything in the background, I point them out to divine justice.

He stands up suddenly, and points with an accusing finger.

The camera pans in a semi-circular movement round the auditorium to follow the direction of his finger . . . pointing at the three AUTHORS.

MACAIRE *quick shot of him, pointing*: . . These are the true authors of the Adrets's crime !

148

Medium shot of the three AUTHORS *who get up, turn their backs to the audience, and go out as one man.*

Long shot of the audience seen from the stage: roars of applause. People are getting up, shouting, laughing. Long shot from the back of the auditorium, with the stage in the background. People are standing and applauding. The curtain is lowered, and then raised again. FREDERICK *bows.*

VOICES : Bravo, Frederick ! . . . Bravo Lemaître ! Bravo ! *Repeated several times.*

The curtain is lowered and then raised again.

In the wings: medium shot of the DIRECTOR, *overjoyed, and the three* AUTHORS, *tight-lipped and bilious.*

DIRECTOR *exuberant* : Ah ! A triumph ! . . . A triumph ! Unforgettable.

AUTHORS *in chorus* : An unprecedented shame !

Shot of the whole stage, seen from the wings. The Curtain rises again. FREDERICK *bows. Applause.*

A FEW VOICES *isolated among the audience* : The authors ! The authors ! The authors ! The authors !

FREDERICK *rapidly comes over to the wings and takes one of the* AUTHORS *by the arm, running back to the front of the stage with him; the two others follow rapidly behind. They walk onto the stage and bow with smiles full of discretion and modesty. Shots of them first from the back, bowing towards the audience, then from the front as the curtain falls.*

The stage seen from the back. (Still on page 130)

The curtain has barely fallen and the smile of the three AUTHORS *fades instantly. Further applause off. The curtain goes up once again. Medium long shot of the stage from the auditorium: the* AUTHORS *promptly regain their modest smiles. The curtain falls for the last time.*

The last applause is dying out.

FREDERICK *suddenly finds himself face to face with the three* AUTHORS.

FREDERICK *smiling at the* AUTHORS : Well, are you happy ?

FIRST AUTHOR : Monsieur, you have outraged us, and only your ignorance prevents you from realising that in outraging us . . .

THE THREE *together* : . . . you have outraged the entire realm of dramatic art !

FIRST AUTHOR: You have plundered our prose, done violence to our verse, trampled on our truisms!

FREDERICK: It all brings good luck!

FIRST AUTHOR: Vulgar creature.

THREE AUTHORS *together*: You must apologise.

FREDERICK: Whenever you like, whenever you like. Tomorrow morning, for example!

> FREDERICK *pushes them aside. At that moment the* DIRECTOR *appears.*

DIRECTOR: Oh, gentlemen! You're not going to fight! It's insane!

FREDERICK: What can one do, since the Holy Trinity considers itself offended, we are going to fight it out with the Holy Trinity! . . . *Still talking to the horrified* DIRECTOR . . . And I rely on you to arrange everything . . . *Very debonair* . . . All these gentlemen have to do is to draw lots, and I'll fight the winner . . . *To the* AUTHORS . . . Gentlemen, I leave the choice of arms to you. Tomorrow, at dawn, I shall be in the chestnut grove with two friends.

> *He bows with dignity and a theatrical flourish, and walks out of shot with a haughty, ironic smile, while the horrified* DIRECTOR *pursues him, crying:*

DIRECTOR *his arms raised to heaven*: No, Frederick! Oh, no! Frederick! Frederick! . . . *His voice fades away.*

> *The camera holds for a moment on the* AUTHORS *dismayed, and extremely uneasy.*
>
> [*A medium shot of* FREDERICK, *coming into frame from the left, as he walks along the corridor to his dressing room. He goes in and closes the door.*] (Shot but cut from versions shown.) *Medium shot of the door of* FREDERICK'S *dressing room:* FREDERICK, *happy to be alone, shuts the door and locks it, and heaves a sigh of relief . . . But he is immediately on the alert again.*

LACENAIRE *off*: Wise precaution!

> *Stupefied,* FREDERICK *turns towards the voice. The camera pans to follow his look to frame* LACENAIRE, *in medium shot, sitting at a table laid for supper for several people. He plays, negligently, with his cane; his linen is, as always, dazzlingly white (special lighting effect) but his clothes are smarter and newer than they used to be. His features are drawn, and his face has aged far too rapidly.*

150

Cut back to FREDERICK *absolutely dumbfounded to find this man here, comfortably installed as if he was in his own home, examining him with curiosity and a tight smile.*

FREDERICK : How did you get in?

The camera pans rapidly towards what LACENAIRE *is holding in his hands, — Phoebe's crescent. Pan back again to* FREDERICK *who leaps forwards; close medium shot of the two of them,* FREDERICK *standing,* LACENAIRE *sitting, very relaxed.* (*Still on page 131*)

FREDERICK : Leave that alone! . . . *He seizes it* . . . It's a souvenir.

LACENAIRE *letting go of the object with affected indifference* : Perhaps it's also a souvenir for me . . . who knows?

FREDERICK *beside himself* : Impossible! You must be either drunk or mad. And first of all, what are you doing here? Who are you?

LACENAIRE *very calm* : My name wouldn't mean anything to you. And since you are famous enough for two, let's leave aside the introductions, and go straight to the object of my visit. Here it is in three words — I need money.

FREDERICK *put out of countenance* : So does everyone else, you know.

LACENAIRE *smiling* : More or less.

As he speaks, FREDERICK, *followed by the camera in close shot, goes to put Phoebe's crescent back on the wall.*

FREDERICK : Perhaps, but I must admit that I don't quite see why you come to me, when I don't know you at all.

LACENAIRE *playing with his cane* : That doesn't matter in the least since I know you. Since the whole of Paris knows you!

FREDERICK *followed by the camera again comes back to the table and picks up a cold chicken; he tears it apart with his hands, and voraciously begins on a leg as he speaks.*

FREDERICK *trying to be modest* : You're very polite, but I'm afraid you're exaggerating.

LACENAIRE *off* : You are already famous . . . and obviously rich . . . *Shot of him* . . . Isn't that a sufficient reason for a man who's down and out to come to you, quite simply, and ask for what he needs.

FREDERICK *standing up and eating* : Down and out?

LACENAIRE *icy and definite* : It's a question of life or death.

FREDERICK *sitting down at the table and pouring himself a drink* : Honestly?

LACENAIRE: Do I look as if I'm joking?

FREDERICK *looking at him, his mouth full*: No! *He takes another swig of his drink.* Listen, I'm far from rich! I can assure you! *He gets up, rubs his hands and leans down towards his topcoat.* But perhaps you've been sent by Fate. *He laughs.* Because last week I had a win on the lottery, and I haven't spent it all yet. You're in luck!

> *He takes the money out of his pocket and approaches* LACENAIRE, *who is still sitting. Shot of the two of them:* FREDERICK *standing facing the camera, and* LACENAIRE *three-quarters back view.*

FREDERICK: Of course, if you were my friend, my brother, I'd say, here you are, take the lot . . . *Showing a wad of money* . . . it's yours. But since I have only had the honour of meeting you, I say to you, we'll share it.

> *He divides the money in two, holds out half to* LACENAIRE, *and puts the rest in his pocket.*

FREDERICK: If this sum can be of any use to you . . . *gently ironic* . . . quite simply, accept it.

> *Close shot of* LACENAIRE, *facing the camera, with* FREDERICK *half out of the picture.* LACENAIRE *gets up and takes the money as if it was his by right.*

LACENAIRE: Thank you. *Then he looks at* FREDERICK *without being able to hide his surprise. Sitting down.* You astonish me. Actors are reputed to be very mean, especially great actors.

FREDERICK *medium close-up, amused*: Well, that's splendid!

> *The camera pans to follow* FREDERICK; *he breaks off a piece of bread and goes on eating.*

FREDERICK: There's still room for improvement!

LACENAIRE *close shot*: Your profession is a very strange one.

> *Close reverse angle shot of* FREDERICK *facing the camera; he takes a piece of meat off the table and begins to eat it.*

FREDERICK: The most glorious of all!

LACENAIRE *dreamily*: Perhaps, but it's very surprising, this ability to make people's hearts beat faster at exactly the same time every evening!

> FREDERICK *sits down and goes on eating.*

FREDERICK *becoming more and more lyrical*: You don't understand anything about it. That's exactly what is so beautiful, so intoxicating about it; to feel one's heart and the hearts of the audience beating together!

LACENAIRE *more and more distant* : What promiscuity. As for me, when occasionally my heart begins to beat, it beats so strongly that there is a quite particular sensuality in knowing that I am the only one to hear it.

FREDERICK *ironic, emptying his glass* : May one ask what the possessor of such a heart does in the world?

LACENAIRE *in profile* : If I told you, you would find it difficult to believe. In my spare time I write plays.

> *Medium close-up of* FREDERICK *eating: he has a reflex of disappointment, and replies, with a certain aggressiveness.*

FREDERICK : Ah, you are an author! . . . and of course you're not well-known.

LACENAIRE *not in the least put out* : Yes, unknown. *He gets up and comes over to* FREDERICK *who is eating and drinking.* But it doesn't worry me in the least. I write light, delicate little pieces . . . *He walks round* FREDERICK . . . and these days people prefer melodramas! *He stops close to* FREDERICK *and smiles; close shot of both of them.* But I have done one thing which I'm weak enough to be rather fond of. One simple little act full of gaiety and melancholy. Two young things who love each other, lose each other, find each other and lose each other again . . . Décor in delicate green, a garden, a fountain!

FREDERICK *in order to say something* : Well, how interesting. *High angle shot of him looking at* LACENAIRE *who is three-quarters backview and half out of shot.* But look, you can tell me now, since we know each other a little better. *He picks his teeth with a fingernail.* Just between us two, this business about the money, was it really a question of life or death?

> *Series of reverse angle shots:* LACENAIRE *low angle,* FREDERICK *high angle.*

LACENAIRE *icy* : Yes. For you.

FREDERICK *surprised* : For me?

LACENAIRE : Yes — if you had had the imprudence to refuse. *He half opens his topcoat and shows, sticking out of an interior pocket the handle of a dagger* . . . And I can promise you that the blade doesn't slide into the handle!

> *High angle shot of* FREDERICK, LACENAIRE *half out of shot,*

more and more dumbfounded: suddenly he bursts into
laughter, bending right over, and hitting his chest.

FREDERICK : And you think that Frederick would have let you do
whatever you wanted?

FREDERICK *gets up; they are facing each other in close shot.*

LACENAIRE *very calm* : Yes, because I did not come alone. *He*
turns towards the back of the dressing room. Avril! . . .

Close shot of the curtain which is pushed aside. AVRIL *comes*
towards the camera, with his flower in his mouth and his
blissful smile.

Medium shot of all three, with the table between them.

FREDERICK: Well, I'll be . . . *Nodding his head, suddenly delighted.*
Unbelievable! It's exactly the 'Brigands Inn'.

LACENAIRE *more and more serious, speaking to* AVRIL : Well, Avril,
are you satisfied?

AVRIL *staring at* FREDERICK *with great round eyes* : Oh yes, I'm
satisfied!

LACENAIRE *to* FREDERICK: I must tell you that this great oaf has the
deepest admiration for you. And the idea of . . . *He makes a gesture*
signifying robbery and murder.

AVRIL : Yes, it made me feel sick!

FREDERICK *more and more delighted* : Really? I'm delighted to
find that there are good fellows in every profession. *To* AVRIL. So
what did you think of the show tonight, the 'brigands' — did
you like it?

AVRIL *blushing* : Er . . .

LACENAIRE : Don't press him, he's a boy who is modest about his
feelings.

FREDERICK : And you? Were you in the audience?

LACENAIRE : Yes.

FREDERICK : Well?

LACENAIRE : It's interesting . . . of course, I don't want to criticise,
but . . .

FREDERICK *interrupting him happily* : Please. It's not every day
that one can have the advice of a specialist . . . a connoisseur. It's
marvellous . . . unhoped for. You must both do me the pleasure of
dining with me. I had prepared a little dinner for the authors, but
now . . .

FREDERICK *takes off his hat and invites them both to sit down.*

154

AVRIL *embarrassed* : Oh! . . . Monsieur Frederick!

LACENAIRE : You're very kind, but we don't wish to force our company on you. Perhaps you want to sleep?

FREDERICK : Sleep, no. But I'm as hungry as a wolf! . . . *tapping on* AVRIL'S *shoulder* . . . Come on, sit down and no fuss.

LACENAIRE : If you insist.

Medium shot of the three of them sitting down. FREDERICK *immediately picks up a bottle of champagne and uncorks it.*

FREDERICK : Anyway, I have to fight a duel in the morning, and I must keep up my strength. *They all shout with laughter as the champagne spurts out in an arc, right across frame.* It must be disagreeable to die hungry. (*Still on page 132*)

LACENAIRE : You're fighting a duel? Who with?

Medium close-up of LACENAIRE *interested, with* FREDERICK *half out of the picture, drinking and replying.*

FREDERICK : With an imbecile!

LACENAIRE : I hope you intend to kill him?

FREDERICK : Oh, if one could kill all the imbeciles!

LACENAIRE *dreaming* : Absolutely. *With a deep sigh, he unfolds his serviette.* And, after all, it would simplify an awful lot of things!

It is dawn, in a clearing in the forest on the outskirts of Paris. General shot, slightly low angle. There is a morning mist on the calm waters of a small lake, and the birds are singing.

Medium shot, and then long shot and a slow pan: a carriage standing in the middle of an avenue bordered with poplars. The lanterns of the carriage still glimmer in the growing light of day. The camera pans smoothly to reveal the clearing; in the centre are five men. Two are sitting on a fallen tree, and the three others are standing up several feet away. Medium shot of the DIRECTOR *of the theatre and a* DOCTOR. *The* AUTHORS *are nervously pacing to and fro. The* DOCTOR *verifies his case of surgical instruments.* (*Still on page 132*) *In front of him, impossible to miss, is an open case of pistols.*

DIRECTOR *to the* AUTHORS : Just at the moment when we have a triumph on our hands!! . . . Remember that if you kill poor Frederick, you're killing the goose that lays the golden eggs!

Medium shot of the three AUTHORS, *slightly low angle: the first* AUTHOR *is standing immobile in the foreground, the two*

155

others pacing up and down, just as they did in the scene of the rehearsal of ' Brigands Inn '.

FIRST AUTHOR *lugubrious*: Remember that the goose that lays the golden eggs has a very good chance of . . .

SECOND AND THIRD AUTHORS *together, as they stop pacing*: . . . killing us as well!

FIRST AUTHOR: Please, gentlemen, you are forgetting that I am the only one who is going to fight!

SECOND AND THIRD AUTHORS: Is it our fault if you are the only one who knows how to use a pistol?

FIRST AUTHOR *not at all sure of himself*: Use a pistol! Use a pistol!
There is the sound of galloping hooves. The DIRECTOR *turns his head. The camera pans, following his glance to frame in medium long shot a carriage which is approaching at a gallop. Medium shot, slightly low angle, of the* AUTHORS.

SECOND AND THIRD AUTHORS: Ah! Here he is! . . .

FIRST AUTHOR *lugubriously looking at his watch*: And for once he's punctual!
Medium shot, fairly high angle, of the road. The carriage stops opposite the clearing. The door opens: FREDERICK *jumps out, still wearing his extraordinary stage costume. He is followed by* LACENAIRE *and* AVRIL. *Medium shot of the* DIRECTOR, *facing the camera in the foreground, and the three* AUTHORS *in the background, also facing the camera.*

DIRECTOR *under his breath*: But he's drunk, for heaven's sake!
All four stare at each other, stupefied. Cut back to a medium long shot of FREDERICK, *who, followed by* LACENAIRE *and* AVRIL, *comes forward with an attempt at dignity, but noticeably staggering. The camera tracks backwards in front of them. They reach the* DOCTOR, *then the* DIRECTOR *and the three* AUTHORS.

FREDERICK *very much the grand gentleman*: Excuse me, gentlemen, I didn't have time to change into black. *Pointing to his friends.* We talked all night. *Grand melodramatic gesture.* A fascinating conversation . . . and the time passed. *The* AUTHORS *stare at each other flabbergasted;* FREDERICK *goes on.* However, we are not here to exchange words . . . but bullets!
He points to LACENAIRE *and* AVRIL *again; they are not walking very straight either.*

156

FREDERICK : I would like to present to you my seconds. Two very brave men whose names you must permit me . . . *In a confiding tone* . . . for political reasons, to keep to myself.

DOCTOR AND DIRECTOR *bowing*: Gentlemen !

LACENAIRE AND AVRIL : Gentlemen !

Under the eye, more and more pathetic, of the FIRST AUTHOR, *the seconds go off left in the direction of the case in which the pistols are glistening, while the* DIRECTOR, *taking* FREDERICK *affectionately by the arm, drags him to one side. The camera pans to frame the two men in close-up, facing the camera.*

DIRECTOR : Look here, you can't do this, you can't be in earnest ! You're not your normal self.

FREDERICK *with dignity*: My normal self . . . never met him !

DIRECTOR *more and more pressing*: After all, have a bit of sense. . . . You're reeling. You can't even walk straight !

FREDERICK *imperturbable*: Doesn't matter in the least. I'm not going far. And then, in this type of ceremony it's always the line you're aiming along that's the shortest distance between two points. *With a huge guffaw.* Isn't it?

FREDERICK goes out of shot. The camera stays on the DIRECTOR, *raising his arms to the heavens.*

[*Medium shot of* FREDERICK'S *carriage, and the horses. After a very short time one of the horses turns its head in the direction of the clearing. Two shots are heard. Low angle shot: frightened by the shots a flock of crows wing their way swiftly over a little thicket.*] (Only the shots are heard in most versions shown.)

It is night time on the ' Boulevard du Temple *'. Medium close-up on a poster for the '* Grand Theatre *', advertising '* THE BRIGANDS INN *'. Diagonally across it is plastered a streamer, with the words '* No Performance *'. The camera zooms back from the poster, to reveal a passer-by reading it and shaking his head. A boy runs past and bumps into the man.*

[MAN *to the* BOY : You're a right little ruffian !

BOY *turning round with an irreverent gesture*: Listen to you ! You should go and see Baptiste !

MAN *shrugging his shoulders*: It's maddening. You never hear anything else these days. Baptiste ! . . . Baptiste !

He goes off.] (This scene was never shot.)

The camera pans to reveal, on the pavement, FREDERICK,
*with a cigar between his teeth, and his right arm in a sling.
He is strolling among the crowd and crosses the street while
the camera stays for a moment on the people in front of the
'* Grand Theatre *', discussing what the '* No Performance *'
sign means. Medium shot, then general shot with the camera
tracking backwards on a crane, of the façade of the '* Theatre
des Funambules *', covered by a gigantic cardboard pierrot
wearing a shoulder band, with the title of the show on it.*

THE RAG AND BONE MAN[1]
Pantomime in Four Tableaux
by M. Cot d'Ordan[2]

*The Pierrot is a vulgar but recognisable representation of
Baptiste's. It is obvious that the theatre façade has been repainted, that there is no platform outside, but just posters
announcing the show like any other theatre.*
*The camera moves backwards again, and frames, from a
slightly high angle, a crowd of would-be theatre-goers, arguing
with the* TICKET SELLER *at the entrance to the theatre.
Medium shot, then sideways travelling shot, following*
FREDERICK *who goes up to the* TICKET SELLER.

TICKET SELLER : But I've told you, it's full up.

AN UNSATISFIED CUSTOMER : And for tomorrow night?

TICKET SELLER : Tomorrow night too, there isn't a seat left.

ANOTHER DISSATISFIED CUSTOMER *grumbling* : Who's ever heard
of such a thing? A ticket seller who won't sell tickets!

The TICKET SELLER *notices* FREDERICK.

TICKET SELLER *recognising* FREDERICK : Oh, Monsieur Frederick,
are you hurt?

FREDERICK *pulls the* TICKET SELLER *off a little to one side.
The camera tracks backwards and sideways to frame them
both in close shot.*

---

[1] Translator's Note: The French title ' Chand d'Habits ' was based on the
Old Clothes Man's cry.

[2] Cot d'Ordan, was an historical character then administrator of the Funambules, and did create this dramatic and macabre pantomime. But in reality
Debureau did not play the Pierrot at this time, because he was in the process
of being tried for manslaughter.

FREDERICK : Oh, it's nothing. I was shooting pigeons . . . and one of them bit me!

TICKET SELLER *winking* : I heard that the pigeon had a wounded wing too. *He smiles.* Is that why you're closed?

FREDERICK : Yes.

TICKET SELLER : Pity! I hear too that the 'Brigand' had an 'accident' last night. They're all talking about it. Listen, it's like it was for Baptiste; it wasn't going particularly well, and then suddenly, you'd never believe it, all Paris is fighting over who'll put their bottoms on the benches.

FREDERICK : But you can find me a place, though, can't you?

TICKET SELLER *worried* : Difficult! *Suddenly his face lights up.* Oh! I've got an idea! Come on. *He leads him off. Fade out.*

> *In a corridor of the* ' Theatre des Funambules ', *the camera tracks backwards in front of* FREDERICK *and the* TICKET SELLER. *Music sounds faintly in the background.*

TICKET SELLER *continuing his story* : Exactly, a young society woman who comes every evening, alone, no one knowing who she is . . . *he winks* . . . to see Baptiste.

FREDERICK : Lucky Baptiste! *Interested.* Is she pretty?

TICKET SELLER *making a gesture in front of his face* : Can't tell. She wears a veil. She comes and she goes, without seeing anyone.

> *He stops in front of the door of the box. So does the camera. He knocks, and without waiting for a reply opens the door. Medium shot of the box, the* TICKET SELLER, FREDERICK *in the background. The* TICKET SELLER *speaks to someone out of shot.*

TICKET SELLER : Do you mind, Madame? Just for once. A chair at the back for someone who is wounded.

> *Reverse angle shot: the box in medium shot as seen from the stage. The* ' person ', *a young woman, dressed very elegantly, with a low décolletage, is recognisable in spite of her veil. It is* GARANCE. *She neither turns round nor replies. The* TICKET SELLER, *behind her, makes a sign to* FREDERICK *to sit down.*

TICKET SELLER *in a low voice* : It's all right.

FREDERICK *also in a low voice* : Thanks.

> *The camera moves backwards to show the box and a part of the auditorium.* FREDERICK *who has not recognised* GARANCE, *leans forward discreetly to get a better look at this mysterious*

creature. Suddenly, medium shot of both of them facing the camera. He jumps. (Still on page 165)

FREDERICK : Garance !

Medium close-up of GARANCE *full face, with* FREDERICK *half out of the picture.*

GARANCE *surprised* : Frederick? . . . What are you doing here?

Reverse angle shot : FREDERICK *in medium close-up, full face; GARANCE half out of shot.*

FREDERICK *smiling and debonair* : Paris is small for those who love each other as we do . . . *Suddenly, he interrupts himself.* But I don't believe it Garance — you treat me like a stranger — you call me ' vous ' ?

Series of reverse angle shots according to the dialogue.

GARANCE *very sweet and a little wearily* : Don't be angry. It's a very long time since I said ' tu ' to anyone.

FREDERICK *coming closer to* GARANCE : Oh ! Desdemona, perfidious creature, who left me, one fine day, in the middle of the street. ' See you this evening, Frederick.' And she disappears for years. *Nodding his head.* And when she decides to reappear she asks innocently, as if I was a stranger, ' What are you doing here? ' But I am here because I never went away. I knew that you would come back, and I've waited here, sitting on this chair, for years !

GARANCE *smiling* : You haven't changed, Frederick.

FREDERICK *moving closer* : Nor have you, Garance. Or rather, yes. *Leaning down towards her.* You've changed. You are even more desirable than before. And I don't know, you're more, more . . .

GARANCE *with sudden tenderness in her voice* : More sophisticated, isn't that what you mean? *Without waiting for a reply.* But what's the matter with your arm? You're wounded?

FREDERICK : It's three times nothing and it's better already. *Suddenly more serious and regarding* GARANCE *with severity.* There are other wounds that take longer to heal. *Close shot of both of them favouring* FREDERICK. GARANCE *is staring at him fixedly.* Only wounds to one's self-respect, perhaps, but wounds all the same ! *Abruptly.* It was with that man, Desdemona, that man with his arms laden with flowers, that you disappeared, wasn't it? And where did you go? Where did he take you, this Nabob? To India, perhaps?

Reverse angle close shot favouring GARANCE; FREDERICK *is*

160

three-quarters backview.

GARANCE *with the utmost naturalness*: It's true, I did go to India. But I didn't stay there very long. I lived for most of the time in England . . . in Scotland.

FREDERICK *bitterly*: I suppose it's beautiful, Scotland?

GARANCE: Yes, it's beautiful. But it's a long way away. And Paris is the only place I love.

Medium shot of both of them facing the camera.

FREDERICK *ironic, lowering his voice*: Paris and its memories! . . . Baptiste, for instance. Baptiste, whom you come here to see every evening.

She shrugs her shoulders without replying, and looks dreamily towards the stage.

FREDERICK: Are you asking me to believe you don't know Frederick Lemaître, too, is on stage every evening?

She looks at FREDERICK *for a moment, and then turns back to the stage. General shot in the direction of the stage. The curtain has just risen, and the décor represents a little square. It is evening. On the right, a house with a flight of steps leading up to the entrance. On the first floor, in the frame of the windows which are very brightly lit, the clear-cut shadows of dancing couples are thrown, like in the Chinese puppet theatres. A carriage, drawn by an ingenious model horse, stops in front of the door: elegantly dressed guests get out.*

Various general shots of the auditorium, full to bursting, the stall and boxes as well as the Gods.

Cut back to the stage, still in long shot, as seen from the stalls. Another carriage stops in front of the entrance to the house. The ' DUCHESS ' (NATALIE), sumptuously dressed, gets out, while BAPTISTE, *who is clinging on to the back of the carriage jumps down as well. The* DUCHESS *goes into the house.* BAPTISTE, *in transports of love, follows her in without hesitation — to come out again immediately, thrown plumb into the middle of the square by two* FLUNKEYS *in livery, who go back inside after having dusted off their hands, to express disgust. Medium long shot of the Gods: the audience shout with laughter. Close shot of* GARANCE *and* FREDERICK *facing the camera.* GARANCE *raises her shining eyes to the gallery and smiles nostalgically.*

GARANCE: Listen to them up in the Gods, Frederick! *Gently shaking her head.* I used to laugh like that once. Yes, I used to burst out laughing, for no reason, without thinking of anything, just laughing. *She sighs.* And now!

FREDERICK: Are you sad?

GARANCE *turning towards* FREDERICK: No, but I'm not gay either. *Smiling a melancholy smile.* A little spring has broken in the music box. *She turns round to the stage again.* The melody is still the same, but the tone is different.

> FREDERICK *looks at* GARANCE, *and then turns towards the stage. Medium long shot of the stage:* BAPTISTE *gets up slowly. Not knowing what to do, he stares enviously at the beautifully dressed guests, who are going into the house. He compares their clothes to his own, and sinks into despair. A man passes, to put out the street lamps, and* BAPTISTE *is left alone, lit only by the lights from the ballroom where silhouettes representing the dancing guests twist round and round.*
>
> *Quick cut, reverse angle long shot, then medium shot of the Gods; the spectators are all silent and attentive.*
>
> *Cut back to the stage: a call on the trumpet makes* BAPTISTE *jump.** BAPTISTE'S *face expresses joy and hope; he turns towards the trumpet call. The camera pans to frame the arrival of the* OLD CLOTHES MAN (*a role played by* ANSELME DEBUREAU, *dressed in a costume inspired by that of Jericho*). BAPTISTE *goes to meet him. The* OLD CLOTHES MAN *stops, happy to find a client so late.* BAPTISTE *chooses a marvellous apple green frock coat, and a superb pair of 'Cossack' breeches; but when it comes to paying he admits that he does not have a sou. Quick cuts to various parts of the audience, which is shrieking with laughter.*
>
> *Close shot of* GARANCE *and* FREDERICK; *the latter leans over to* GARANCE.

FREDERICK: He really is marvellous!

---

* The script allowed for the cry of the Old Clothes Man, off — 'Chand d'Habits, Chand d'Habits!' which was not really a heresy because this cry would have been the only words pronounced and those not even on stage, and it was intended by the author (Cot d'Ordan), but Carné and Barrault preferred to keep the mime as pure and silent as possible.

General shot of the stage: the OLD CLOTHES MAN *is furious, and wants to go on his way, but* BAPTISTE *begs him for the clothes and, clinging to him, desperately pulls out of its scabbard an old National Guard sabre that the* OLD CLOTHES MAN *was carrying peaceably under his arm. The two men are face to face; the* OLD CLOTHES MAN *is terrified, and* BAPTISTE *carried away by what seems to be the intervention of fate, throws a glance towards the window of the ballroom to give himself courage. Quick cut to a general shot of the audience: they are holding their breath. Cut back to a medium long shot of the stage; the* OLD CLOTHES MAN, *terrified, staggers back before* BAPTISTE *who advances menacingly, his expression suddenly quite different, and very frightening. Close shot of* FREDERICK *and* GARANCE.

GARANCE : It's funny, he is gentleness itself! How can he look so cruel?

Cut back to the stage. Suddenly BAPTISTE *plunges the blade into the body of the* OLD CLOTHES MAN, *who collapses on the ground.** BAPTISTE *stands immobile, his eyes wide, in front of the body of the* OLD CLOTHES MAN. (Still on page 165)

FREDERICK *close-up* : What a technique!

GARANCE *close-up* : Baptiste has no technique; he's not acting; he's inventing dreams!

Close shot of both of them facing the camera.

FREDERICK *slightly bitter, leaning over towards* GARANCE : You love him, don't you?

GARANCE *in a low voice full of tenderness* : Since the first day I left, not a single day has passed when I didn't think of him!

FREDERICK *stares at* GARANCE *with a hostility which is quite new to him, then he turns away again to look at the show. The camera follows his look to frame the stage in long shot, as seen from the box. At last* BAPTISTE *decides to drag the body of the* OLD CLOTHES MAN *into the wings, like an animal dragging a victim into his lair. Very long shot of the*

---

*Translator's Note: At one point during the writing of the script, Carné and Barrault wanted to show Debureau so involved in this part that he ends by killing the real Jericho.

stage seen from the back of the auditorium. Applause bursts out, some spectators stand up to clap more easily, while in the background the curtain falls. Bustle in the auditorium, and the atmosphere of the beginning of the interval.

[*Immediately, sellers of food and sweets, and waiters with their trays surge into the auditorium crying their wares.*

SALESMEN : Fifteen minutes interval! Ask for the programme . . . Caramels, boiled sweets . . . beer, lemonade, white wine. Here are hot apple turnovers, still steaming.]

(In fact, the sequence ends with a quick high angle shot of the auditorium, but the salesmen are not particularly visible. The cries, which were not filmed, had been dubbed into the original soundtrack.)

Fade out. Close shot of the box from the front: FREDERICK *looks at* GARANCE, *shaking his head; then he questions her.*

FREDERICK : And does he know that you come here to see him?

GARANCE : No. He has his life and I have mine . . . so what good would it be?

Medium close-up of FREDERICK; *he looks at* GARANCE, *off screen, for a long time; then his face expresses the most profound astonishment.*

FREDERICK : Oh! It's unbelievable, what's happening to me! It's enough to make you turn inside out . . . to burst!

GARANCE *quick close-up* : What's the matter?

FREDERICK *medium close-up of him, she half out of shot* : I think I'm jealous. No, I don't know . . . I've never felt anything like it. It's heavy, it's unpleasant. It gets hold of you by the heart . . . The head wants to defend itself . . . and . . . hop! it's gone, with the rest of them!

Reverse angle shot of GARANCE, *who is staring blankly at* FREDERICK, *silent. Then close-up of the two of them:* FREDERICK *moves his face close to* GARANCE; *he talks almost into her ear, but never stops staring into her eyes.*

FREDERICK : Do you hear, Garance . . . there, just a moment ago, I was jealous, because of Baptiste, because of you . . . yes, I was jealous! . . . So then, in one fell swoop, regrets flew in! That man, that traveller, who took you away, and I who let you go! And with it all, to make sense out of it all, Baptiste, who acts like a god! Oh, believe me, I didn't want him to act like a pig, but after

164

all, do you understand, if he could have been . . .

GARANCE *interrupting* : Yes, I understand. Just a little bit bad.

FREDERICK : Bad, no ! But, well . . . mediocre. That would have made me feel better. *He smiles.* Well, there's one piece of luck, when you talk it stops. *He sighs.*

GARANCE : You see — it's not so serious. Just a little spasm . . . you're cured already.

Medium shot: FREDERICK *stands up. His face lights up again, he is inspired. The camera pans to follow him in close shot as he walks up and down the box, talking.*

FREDERICK : Cured ! Why do you want me to be cured so quickly ? And what if it pleased me, if it was useful for me to be jealous . . . useful and even necessary? *Suddenly feverish and exalted.* Thank you, Garance. *Close-up of her still sitting down, imperturbable. He continues, off.* Thanks to you, thanks to all of you, I shall be able to play Othello ! *Cut back to him.* I have been trying to find the character, but I didn't feel him. He was a stranger. *He chuckles.* There it is, now he's a friend, he's a brother. I know him . . . I have him in my grasp ! *He goes to the far end of the box and raises his arms to heaven.* Othello ! . . . *Cut to* GARANCE, *and resume on him.* The dream of my life . . . *He comes back towards her and leans down; shot of the two of them.* After you, Desdemona, of course, I shall clasp Baptiste to my heart, at least I owe him that, eh ? Do you want me to tell him anything from you ?

GARANCE : Really, Frederick !

FREDERICK : Oh, I'm speaking seriously. I'm jealous, it's true, but I understand how things are, and then he's married, he has a child, that consoles me ! While the other . . . *He stands upright again.* Ah, the other ! . . . the other ! . . . *A pause, then, smiling* . . . Well, Garance?

GARANCE *close-up; after a hesitation* : Tell him something about me. And if you see that he seems interested, tell him that I am passing through Paris, that I'm leaving again soon, and that I would be happy, so happy, if he came to say hello.

Close shot of FREDERICK *near the door of the box; he agrees, smiling, with a nod, and goes out.*

In the wings of the ' Funambules ' the atmosphere is the same as it used to be, but the walls have been repainted, and the general impression is less squalid. Stagehands are carrying scenery around. Some extras are dressed as society people, and some as footmen. Still the same conglomeration of unlikely and picturesque objects. The stagehands are changing the décor and setting up the drawing room where the dance is taking place. On the centre of the stage the DIRECTOR *is supervising the change of scene. He still looks the same; he has hardly aged, and is wearing a new suit. The camera pans to frame the arrival of* FREDERICK *as seen by the* DIRECTOR *who is pleased to see him, and immediately goes to greet him. Close shot of the two of them.*

DIRECTOR *arms raised to the heavens* : It's you, ungrateful wretch, after so many years! . . . *He embraces him and seems delighted.* Well, we won't reproach the prodigal son who returns to the . . . *He stops the old* STAGE MANAGER *who is passing and suddenly shouts.* Stage Manager, don't forget Alexis : he came on stage drunk, made a disturbance, and broke a Chinese vase, five francs fine !

> FREDERICK, *delighted to come back to his ' first backstage ', walks towards the camera looking round, while the* DIRECTOR *is talking to the* STAGE MANAGER, *but the* DIRECTOR *quickly catches him up, with the camera tracking to follow.*

FREDERICK *smiling* : You've increased your tariff !

DIRECTOR : Well, after all, noblesse oblige, we're so successful now ! *Then looking at him with a protective eye.* But you too, my ' little one ', it seems things aren't going so badly with you either. Fine ! Perfect ! Bravo ! *Suddenly he turns and shouts off screen.* Baptiste ! Baptiste ! . . .

> *Medium shot of a corner of the wings:* BAPTISTE *in costume,* NATALIE, *and a little boy of about five or six, are leaning against the wheels of a carriage, the little boy is on the coachman's seat.* BAPTISTE *turns round, recognises* FREDERICK, *and comes to greet him, moved and astounded. He goes off screen.*

BAPTISTE : Frederick !

Medium shot of BAPTISTE, FREDERICK, *the* DIRECTOR.

FREDERICK : Baptiste !

> *Without hesitation, they fall into each other's arms; then move apart.*

BAPTISTE : Frederick, it's you ! You've come !

FREDERICK : Yes, you see, I've taken the first step ! *Pointing to his arm in its sling.* And on one hand, into the bargain!

BAPTISTE : Oh, not the first step! *Gently shaking his head.* I've already come to applaud you several times.

FREDERICK *extremely surprised . . . and delighted* : No! . . . and you didn't come round to say hello?

> *Close shot of the group with* BAPTISTE *full face and the others half out of the picture.*

BAPTISTE : I didn't dare. And then, each time, I was so moved, so overwhelmed. You've become a great actor, Frederick; the greatest of them all.

FREDERICK *with false modesty* : Oh, come on, not quite.

BAPTISTE : Oh, yes! . . . Yes, yes. You do prodigious things. Really!

FREDERICK *same shot, but reverse angle, favouring* FREDERICK : But it's you who are prodigious, Baptiste. There are a lot of great actors. *Catching himself.* Well, let's say, several. But mimes . . . before you, there weren't any. It's marvellous, you are the only one. You invented everything, by yourself!

> *Medium shot of the three of them.*

BAPTISTE : I'm glad you like my work.

> *Suddenly,* FREDERICK *recognises, a few yards out of shot,* NATALIE.

FREDERICK : Oh! It's Natalie!

> *He goes forward. The camera pans towards her, then reverse angle shot of* FREDERICK *backview going towards* NATALIE *as she stands by the carriage. The little boy is still sitting on the coachman's seat. In the background is* ANSELME DE-BUREAU.

FREDERICK *jovial* : Oh, how beautiful you've grown, Natalie!

NATALIE *smiling* : I'm not beautiful, Frederick. I'm happy, that's all. (*Still on page 166*)

> *Medium long shot of the group, with* ANSELME, BAPTISTE *and the* DIRECTOR, *half out of the picture.*

FREDERICK : Oh! Beauty and happiness go together, you're right. *Pointing to the child.* Is this your little boy? *To the* CHILD. What's your name?

CHILD : Baptiste.

FREDERICK : Baptiste! Just like your father!

> *Close-up of* NATALIE, *facing the camera glowing with joy.* FATHER DEBUREAU *must have his say, and as he pushes*

forward, his costume becomes more noticeable, it is his stage costume as the OLD CLOTHES MAN; *medium shot, but taking in the whole group.*

DEBUREAU *delirious with pride* : Astonishing family, isn't it? . . . *Taking off his hat to* FREDERICK. I salute you, Frederick, and I mark with a white stone the happy day that the greatest actor in Europe and other countries finally came to pay a visit to the incontestable masters of world pantomime !

> *He places a hand, with a kingly gesture, on* BAPTISTE'S *shoulder. They all laugh.*

FREDERICK : Etcetera . . . etcetera !

> *Medium long shot of a door in the wings which opens to let in* JERICHO, *the real* OLD CLOTHES MAN. *He seems to be drunk. He looks much older. He staggers unsteadily towards the camera.*

OLD CLOTHES MAN : Hello, everybody ! . . . Here's old Jericho, known as the Wild Boar, known as the One who Sleeps by Himself !

> *The camera pans to frame the group again, and the* OLD CLOTHES MAN *appears in the background.*

BAPTISTE *on edge* : Here he is again ! *Pulling* FREDERICK *aside* Come over here. I can't stand that man . . . His voice makes me shudder, and the sight of him makes me sick.

[BAPTISTE *turning towards* NATALIE : I've told you before, I don't want to see him here any more.

NATALIE *very gentle* : Oh, come on, we can't turn him out. He's been with us ever since the bad old days.

BAPTISTE *stormy and bitter* : Bad days indeed !]

> (Included in the script, and partially shot, with Robert Le Vigan as Jericho, but cut out in the editing. Le Vigan was originally cast as Jericho, but disappeared at the Liberation when he was suspected of having collaborated, and the part was taken over by Pierre Renoir.)

> *The camera pans to frame the* OLD CLOTHES MAN *approaching* ANSELME DEBUREAU. *Tight close shot of the two of them.*

OLD CLOTHES MAN *to* FATHER DEBUREAU *aggressively* : Ah ! There you are, plunderer, body snatcher !

ANSELME DEBUREAU *very dignified* : You're not going to start again, are you?

OLD CLOTHES MAN *seizing* DEBUREAU *by the lapel*: You should be ashamed! You stole my shape! You stole my identity!

ANSELME DEBUREAU *pulling himself free, still with dignity*: You must be out of your mind. You're not the only Old Clothes Man in Paris, you know. And it was you yourself who provided the costume!

OLD CLOTHES MAN: Ah! But I didn't realise what you were going to do with it. When I think that every evening Baptiste murders a poor old man like me, . . . and just to entertain people, too! What an example to set!

ANSELME DEBUREAU *more and more on his dignity*: Be quiet, my friend. You're drunk, and you're talking nonsense. You'd be well advised to go to sleep.

> *He shakes himself free and walks out of shot. The camera remains on the* OLD CLOTHES MAN, *who looks around him, sad and vindictive at the same time.*

OLD CLOTHES MAN *to* NATALIE, *who is standing close to him*: Perhaps I am drunk, but that doesn't stop me from knowing the difference between right and wrong. *Suddenly, he notices the little boy on his seat. He goes up to the carriage. Medium close-up of the child, with* JERICHO *in the foreground, backview and half out of shot.* Why don't you ever say hello to old Papa Joshua? You're like your father, aren't you? You despise me, you ignore me! *Close-up of* JERICHO *as he turns towards* NATALIE, *out of shot.* What's Baptiste got against me, eh? Natalie? What's he got against me?

> *Medium close-up of* NATALIE, *full face;* JERICHO *half out of shot, and a series of reverse angle shots according to the dialogue.*

NATALIE *shrugging her shoulders*: He's got nothing against you . . . except that he thinks you interfere too much in other people's business.

OLD CLOTHES MAN *with an unpleasant expression*: What of it? Is it any of his business, what's my business and what isn't? I've always lived alone, so, of course, I ' interest myself in other people ' . . . it's only natural. *Suddenly tearful and bitter* Always alone, that's no life! Nobody ever loved me, nobody, zero, nothing! Even if I was a widower, at least I'd have some memories . . . *with a cruel, drunken glitter in his eyes.* But not a single one of them would have anything to do with me. They all preferred little fly-by-nights, little lechers! . . .

As he speaks, he slowly moves away from NATALIE. *But suddenly, he comes back towards her again. Medium close-up of the two of them.*

OLD CLOTHES MAN : Listen, Natalie, I'll tell you something . . . *Lowering his voice.* Yes, all right, it's none of my business, but if it's for your own good, eh?

NATALIE *pulling herself free* : Leave me alone, with your stories!

OLD CLOTHES MAN : Listen all the same. This one isn't long. Here it is : Garance has come back, she's here, in box seven, and she's waiting for Baptiste.

NATALIE *astonished and distressed* : Garance!

OLD CLOTHES MAN : Yes, like the flower! *He walks away; pan to follow him as he turns round.* Box seven, don't forget.

Cut back to NATALIE, *who no longer glows with happiness, but seems to have shrunk in on herself. When she can pull herself together again, she turns towards her son, who is still sitting on the coachman's seat.*

NATALIE : Baptiste!

BAPTISTE *the son* : Mama!

NATALIE *lifting the child down and putting him on the ground* : Baptiste, listen . . . you . . .

Cut.

In the wings, near the stage, medium shot of BAPTISTE *and* FREDERICK *facing the camera and walking along with the camera tracking backwards in front of them. The two men seem to be gay, happy to have met again and to be exchanging memories.*

FREDERICK : Yes, it's true, you know . . . I've often regretted the Funambules; what about you? Do you enjoy thinking of the time we used to work together? *Medium close-up of both of them facing the camera.*

BAPTISTE *after a slight hesitation* : Yes, Frederick, I like to think of those times. *He seems to be frozen, facing the camera.*

FREDERICK : Er . . . er . . . then you're not angry with me?

BAPTISTE *surprised* : Me? Why should I be angry with you?

FREDERICK *machiavellian* : Garance!

BAPTISTE, *after a moment, he seems to be coming out of a dream,*

174

and has a curious gleam in his eyes : Garance! . . . *A pause.* What's
past is past. *Sad.* All that seems so long ago, now.
> *Cut.*
> *Medium shot from the auditorium towards* GARANCE'S *box.*
> *She is anxious and impatient. Suddenly there is a knock on the*
> *door.*

GARANCE *turning round suddenly* : Come in!
> *The door of the box seen at an adult's eye level. The door*
> *opens apparently by itself. Then the camera pans down to*
> *reveal* NATALIE'S LITTLE BOY.

LITTLE BAPTISTE : Good evening, Madame.
> *Cut to* GARANCE, *astonished, then cut back to a medium*
> *close-up of the* LITTLE BOY. *Reverse angle shots according to*
> *the dialogue.*

LITTLE BAPTISTE *sweet and straightforward, and not in the least
embarrassed* : I've got a message for you. I've come to tell you that
we all three live very happily together, Mama and Papa and me.

GARANCE, *she too, seems to shrink* : And your father sent you to tell
me that?

LITTLE BAPTISTE : No, it was Mama. But Mama, Papa and me,
it's all the same!
> *Medium close-up of* GARANCE, *unable to speak, and cut back*
> *to the* CHILD.

LITTLE BAPTISTE : It's true what Mama said!

GARANCE *sad* : What did she say?

LITTLE BAPTISTE : That you were beautiful! . . . *He smiles at her.*
When I'm grown up, I'll get married, and I'll marry a girl like you,
or like Mama. If there are any, of course!
> *Close shot of* GARANCE *in profile. She holds out her hand to*
> LITTLE BAPTISTE, *who comes in from the right, comes close*
> *to her, and puts his hand in hers.*

GARANCE : You're a very sweet little boy.

LITTLE BAPTISTE *following his own train of thought* : Are you
married?

GARANCE : No.

LITTLE BAPTISTE : So you haven't got a little boy?

GARANCE : No, I haven't got a little boy.

LITTLE BAPTISTE *serious* : So you're all alone then?

> GARANCE, *more and more distressed, gently caresses* LITTLE

175

Baptiste's *hair. The three knocks announcing that the curtain is about to rise, can be heard.*

GARANCE : Yes, I'm all alone . . .

General shot of the stage. The curtain rises. The décor represents a large drawing room. Footmen wander around with trays of ' refreshments '. There are a few couples dancing, and among them is the ' DUCHESS '. Medium shot of FREDERICK and BAPTISTE leaning against a piece of scenery, in the same place.

FREDERICK : And you aren't intrigued by this woman who comes every night to see you? *Smiling.* Perhaps you're used to it?

BAPTISTE *shrugs his shoulders, smiling. Long shot of the stage as seen by them, therefore from the ' courtyard ' side of the wings: the show is going on. Cut back to them, full face. The STAGE MANAGER passes in front of them, busily as usual.*

STAGE MANAGER : It'll be you in a minute, Baptiste.

Cut to the stage: NATALIE is waltzing with a young admirer. Cut back to BAPTISTE and FREDERICK in close shot, full face.

FREDERICK : Listen, Baptiste. I should have told you before, but that woman is Garance ! . . .

The camera zooms forward to frame both of them in a close-up. BAPTISTE is paralysed.

FREDERICK : She has come back, and she's got to go away again. So she would like to see you !

Medium shot of NATALIE on stage, who drops her fan on purpose as she waltzes. Medium long shot from the audience: BAPTISTE rushes forward, picks up the fan and gives it back to NATALIE, who smiles. BAPTISTE becomes braver, and sweeps her away in a waltz. (Still on page 167) Medium close-up of them dancing; an expression of true despair is on BAPTISTE's face. NATALIE gazes at him anxiously. BAPTISTE suddenly misses his step and stops dancing. Close-up of her terribly upset. Close-up of him overwhelmed with despair.

NATALIE *in a low voice :* What's the matter, Baptiste?

Long shot of the scene: BAPTISTE abandons NATALIE, and rushes off stage.

[BAPTISTE *pushes aside a footman who is carrying a tray of refreshments. The tray falls down with a loud clatter.*

176

NATALIE *cries*: Baptiste!] (Cut to avoid repetition of the scene in the first half.)

> *General shot slightly low angle of the Gods; the audience look at each other in astonishment. Then a voice shouts in direction of the stage.*

A VOICE: Hey ... Baptiste! ... Baptiste! *Cut.*

> *Medium long shot of the corridor outside the boxes.* BAPTISTE *rushes towards the camera, passing his son without even noticing him. The little boy is coming back, and looks after his father, astonished.* BAPTISTE *in the foreground opens the door of Box Seven.*
>
> *Immediately the shouts of the audience can be heard, demanding:* 'Baptiste!' *Close shot of the box seen from the audience.* BAPTISTE *is on the threshold, stunned. Reverse angle shot of the chair* GARANCE *had been sitting in; it is as empty as the box. Cut back to* BAPTISTE *in close shot; utterly crushed, he lowers his head, while the voices in the audience, more and more of them, cry louder and louder. Desperate and exasperated,* BAPTISTE *covers his ears.*
>
> *In the entrance hall of the* COUNT'S *town house, at night. The entrance hall is semi-circular. On the right is a majestic staircase. The front door is in the background, seen in a medium shot, slightly high angle. The door opens and* GARANCE *comes in. She is wearing the same dress that she had on at the* 'Funambules', *with a cape thrown over it. The* FOOTMAN *says a few words, which cannot be heard, to her, and gestures with his head to the first floor.* GARANCE *goes towards the staircase and climbs it rapidly. The camera pans to follow her and reveals the first floor landing; sitting on a sofa, a man, motionless, three-quarters back to the camera, seems to be waiting for* GARANCE. *His position and the shadows, prevent him from being recognised at once.* GARANCE *passes him, then, instinctively sensing a presence, she turns round. Medium shot of* GARANCE *and the man, in the background, as he gets up. The light falls onto his face, and it turns out to be* LACENAIRE.

LACENAIRE: Good evening, my angel.

GARANCE: Oh! ... Pierre-François.

LACENAIRE: What? ... *He is facing the camera, she is in the foreground, three-quarters backview; he comes towards her smiling.*

Ah! Yes . . . Pierre-François . . . yes, yes. Excuse me, Garance —
I've had so many names that sometimes I forget them myself! A
childish precaution, as a matter of fact — the police are so
inefficient. *Smiling more broadly and playing with his cane.* Unlike
mine. I know a lot . . . for instance, Garance, when you came back
I knew immediately . . . Oh, I knew where you were hiding, my
angel, and with whom!

GARANCE *ironic and indifferent*: One can hide nothing from you.

Close shot of the two of them.

LACENAIRE *gently aggressive, looking around him*: I know too
that my beautiful angel is in a cage . . . and in the most beautiful
cage in Paris . . . Not that I'm throwing any stones. I too have
spent a considerable time in prison lately, and a provincial one at
that! *She stares at him, then plays with her fan.* What? Not even
the shadow of a smile? Yet I used to amuse you. Have you lost
your gaiety, or are you unpleasantly surprised to see me?

GARANCE *very straightforward*: No! On the contrary, I'm glad
to see you. *Dreamily, she turns her back on* LACENAIRE *and leans
against an armchair.* Yes, it reminds me . . .

LACENAIRE: . . . A whole period of your life! *He sniggers.*

Medium long shot: LACENAIRE *walks along the landing.*

GARANCE *in the foreground*: Yes . . . those were easy, happy days
. . . life was sweet.

LACENAIRE *turning round*: Be careful, my angel, it's not good to
look at the past. You look at your own past . . . *She sits down; he
stands near her, leaning against a column* . . . and it leaps up into
your face like a mad cat!

Slightly high angle shot of GARANCE *as she takes off her cape.*
LACENAIRE *is in the foreground, backview.*

GARANCE: [I have nothing to fear because . . .] (Cut during the
shooting) All the same, I had the luck to be happy, in spite of
everything!

LACENAIRE: In the old days.

GARANCE: Don't be stupid. The old days and now are the same
thing. Time has nothing to do with happiness.

Reverse angle shot favouring LACENAIRE.

LACENAIRE: Really? And the man in white? Your ' friend ', the
acrobat, do you think that he is happy too? *Medium shot: he takes
three steps towards her.* When I think that I had the absurd idea

of killing him, the acrobat! Idiotic, don't you agree? You might just as well shoot a draught, a ray of moonlight! *He becomes gayer and gayer, like someone who regrets not having carried out a good practical joke.* And as for the other one, yes, Frederick, imagine, my angel, I thought of him too . . . I even went to see him : I invented rather an amusing pretext.

GARANCE : Might one be told?

LACENAIRE : Of course. I said to myself : ' Here is a man that I don't know; I will ask him for some money. He will refuse . . .' and . . .!

GARANCE *ironic* : And he gave you some!

LACENAIRE : Yes, and he gave me a lot! I was astounded.

GARANCE *close-up of her, full face* : You see, there are some kind people.

LACENAIRE *medium shot of the two of them* : People . . . Actors aren't ' people ', they're everybody and nobody at the same time, actors! . . . *Becoming aggressive again* . . . People . . . society people, for instance, I suppose they're people! *Staring insistently at* GARANCE. Count Edward de Monteray, for instance, one of the richest and most brilliant men in France . . . [Great traveller, famous collector and lover of engravings, excellent horseman, billiard champion, unbeatable with swords or pistols.] (Cut during the shooting.)

    GARANCE *gets up. Shot of the two of them face to face.*

GARANCE *nodding her head* : You've changed, Pierre-François.

LACENAIRE : Me?

GARANCE : Yes. In the old days you spoke always of yourself and rarely of others. *Smiling.* Why don't you tell me what's been happening to you?

    She moves towards the camera. He follows her. She goes out of shot while he stays in the foreground facing the camera.

LACENAIRE : I have become famous! Yes, I have pulled off a few fairly sensational crimes, and more than once the name of Lacenaire has ornamented the pages of the Law Chronicles. Lacenaire, for whom the police are at this minute searching the provinces, and who is with his guardian angel, in his good old city of Paris!

    Reverse angle shot: GARANCE, *her back to the camera, approaches a large, bevelled mirror on the wall. She is seen in reflection, facing the camera. Behind her,* LACENAIRE, *in close shot.* (*Still on page 167*)

GARANCE *ironic* : But it's glory, Pierre-François!

LACENAIRE *very serious* : Yes, it's beginning. But thinking it over, I should all the same have preferred a resounding literary success!

GARANCE : Never satisfied, Pierre-François!

LACENAIRE *leaning towards her* : It's said, isn't it, that the Count of Monteray is interested in the arts and is a very generous patron? *Dreamily.* I'd love to meet him.

GARANCE *suddenly anxious* : Do you think that it would be any use?

LACENAIRE *smiling* : Don't worry; I won't ask for anything, but I'd like to know this man who has placed the cold hand of wealth up on the white shoulder of my guardian angel!

> GARANCE *turns towards* LACENAIRE. *The camera leaves the mirror and pans to frame them again face to face.*

GARANCE : Don't you worry, I have been bought, but with no strings attached; I'm still free!

> *She starts to move. The camera remains on him, he half-smiles, bitterly.*

LACENAIRE : Perhaps, and that's exactly what annoys me.

> *Medium long shot:* GARANCE *is picking up her cape, when* LACENAIRE *comes up to her and seizes her arm almost violently.*

LACENAIRE *bitter and feverish* : You can't imagine, Garance, how painful it is for me to have found you again, and above all that you haven't changed! I would have been so much happier to see you spoiled, cheapened, disappointed, turned into an idiot by money! Like that I could have gone on living, with a good conscience, with my idea of what people are like.

GARANCE *using the same tone that* LACENAIRE *uses to* AVRIL : My poor Pierre-François!

LACENAIRE : You think that I'm a monster, don't you?

GARANCE : Perhaps . . . but you aren't the only one.

> *Long shot of the landing, with* GARANCE *and* LACENAIRE *in the centre.*

LACENAIRE : Alas!

> GARANCE *leaves* LACENAIRE *and goes towards her rooms. The camera pans to follow her and reveals a long and imposing series of rooms which lead off one another.*

180

LACENAIRE, *left alone, prepares to descend the grand staircase, but suddenly he stops: he has noticed . . . High angle
long shot of the hall as seen by* LACENAIRE : *by the door*
COUNT EDWARD DE MONTERAY *gives his hat and cloak to the*
FOOTMAN. *He looks in the direction of the landing, then walks
over to the staircase, with great dignity. The camera is at the
bottom of the staircase. The* COUNT *climbs with his back to
the camera, while* LACENAIRE *begins to come down, playing
with his cane. The two men meet in the middle of the staircase. It is the* COUNT *who speaks first, as* LACENAIRE *has passed
him, very coldly, without a word. Medium shot of the two of
them, favouring the* COUNT, *who is two steps above* LACENAIRE.
*The latter turns at the first word, and stops. Then, according
to the dialogue, reverse angle shots: high angle and low angle
shots of the two men together.*

COUNT *surprised and distant* : Monsieur . . .

LACENAIRE *very much at ease* : Edward de Monteray, I believe?

COUNT : That is my name.

LACENAIRE : I burned with desire to see you, Monsieur. *He looks
him up and down with tranquil insolence and takes in everything
from head to foot with insulting care.* Now I have done so, and
behold me satisfied. *(Still on page 168)*

COUNT *phlegmatic, pretending to take it as a joke* : Amusing ! . . .
Yes, amusing and unexpected. May I know, however, to whom I
have the honour . . ?

LACENAIRE *turns round and is about to continue on down.*

LACENAIRE : Oh ! . . . to nobody, Monsieur, nobody. All that is of
no importance !

He goes down two or three steps. The COUNT *goes on upstairs.
The camera moves slightly backwards to keep them both in
shot.*

COUNT *turning around again towards* LACENAIRE : I don't think
you will be surprised if I tell you that I find your manner extremely
distasteful ! What are you doing here, Monsieur? . . . *He puts on
his monocle haughtily.* Who are you?

Close high angle shot of LACENAIRE, *and the* COUNT *half out of
shot and three-quarters backview. Then a series of reverse
angle shots according to the dialogue. The close shot of the*
COUNT *in low angle.*

LACENAIRE *smiling* : Don't you find it an absurd question, to ask people who they are?

COUNT *stupefied* : What?

LACENAIRE *continuing* : That is no doubt why they always reply quite beside the point. Yes, they choose the simplest answer : name, Christian names, titles . . . but what they really are . . . *winking with unpleasant familiarity* . . . really, at the bottom of their hearts, they keep quiet about . . . they hide carefully.

COUNT *disdainfully* : I presume you are speaking about yourself?

LACENAIRE : No, for everybody, and for you as well. I will even add that I find your manner extremely indiscreet. After all you don't even know me, and yet you take the liberty of asking me who I am. It's unbelievable!

COUNT : You need go no further, Monsieur. Just tell me where two of my friends can wait on you tomorrow . . .

LACENAIRE *interrupting him brusquely* : Useless . . . I am not the sort of man with whom one fights duels . . . absolutely not.

COUNT *more and more disdainful* : Better and better — things are much clearer now.

> *High angle shot of* LACENAIRE, *closer than before; the* COUNT *almost entirely out of shot. Reverse angle close shots according to the dialogue.*

LACENAIRE : Or rather, I always reserve for myself the choice of arms. Yes, I choose one, one alone, and I keep it for myself, . . . *Putting his hand casually on his breast, and exposing the handle of a dagger* . . . on me . . . and I only kill when the outcome is certain, and when I choose. *He plays with his cane.*

COUNT : Obviously, it's more expeditious.

LACENAIRE : To each his own method, don't you agree?

COUNT : Indeed, yes . . . *with a smile full of contempt* . . . Well, in these conditions, I presume you have nothing further to say to me! *He calls.* Valentin!

> *Reverse angle, medium long high angle shot: the two men on the staircase, and the entrance hall below.*

LACENAIRE : I would also like to warn you that I am not the sort of man who is thrown out. *He puts his hand inside his jacket.* And it would distress me to have to kill a servant.

COUNT : You needn't worry : Valentin is an old retainer, and I am fond of him.

He turns his head to the left in the direction of the hall. General shot, slightly high angle; the camera, on the ground in the hall, frames half out of shot in the foreground, VALENTIN *coming to the bottom of the stairs.*

COUNT : Valentin? See Monsieur out, would you?

The COUNT *climbs a few more steps.* LACENAIRE *watches with eyes full of hate for a moment, and then starts to descend. Close shot of the landing: the* COUNT, *on the first floor, turns round towards the camera, and looks, still very haughty, down below. Medium long high angle shot, following his look;* LACENAIRE *raises his head towards the camera, and smiles towards the* COUNT *as he crosses the threshold.*

The camera follows the movement of the COUNT *as he turns his head, indignant and angry. Medium long shot panning to follow him as he starts down the corridor* GARANCE *had taken.*

Corridor: long shot of another corridor, equally luxurious: the COUNT, *with his back to the camera, goes up to a door. Someone can be heard singing. The* COUNT *stands for an instant with his ear to the door.* GARANCE *is singing the song she used to sing, but with a sad, almost heartbroken sound.*

GARANCE *singing, off* : I am what I am,
            I drink when I thirst,
            And when I want to laugh,
            I laugh fit to burst.

After having paused for another moment to listen, the COUNT *knocks on the door. The singing stops immediately.*

The singing starts again, but stops when the COUNT *knocks again.*

The COUNT *opens the door.*

The camera follows the movement of the door as it opens, and then as the COUNT *shuts it behind him. The camera pans to follow him into* GARANCE'S *boudoir, and reveals* GARANCE, *in medium shot, sitting at her dressing table, in a négligé, with her back to the camera, and her hair falling down her back. The* COUNT *takes* GARANCE'S *hand, and bows to kiss it.*

COUNT : Good evening, Garance.

GARANCE *seen in reflection in the mirror* : Good evening, my friend.

COUNT *looking at her* : Curious, Garance. When I am not there you

183

sing. But as soon as I arrive you are silent!

GARANCE : What do you expect, my dear? You only like classical music.

COUNT : Alas, our tastes are different!

He comes back to the centre of the room, in medium long shot. Then long shot of the boudoir with the dressing table and GARANCE *in the background. On the left there is a divan fitted into the wall. A fireplace is on the right, and in the centre of the room a low table. The* COUNT *goes over to the table, opens a magnificent jar of tobacco, and fills his pipe as he is talking to* GARANCE, *with his back turned to her, so that he is in the foreground, and she in the background on the left.*

COUNT : Might I ask where you spent the evening, Garance?

GARANCE : At the ' Funambules ', my dear.

COUNT : Again.

GARANCE : And you, Edward, I am sure that you went again to that horrible bear baiting.

COUNT : Horrible is too strong a word for it. Three dogs, and a mangy bear thrown to them like a bone! No sport at all . . . sheer butchery. I passed a very dreary evening. *He turns towards her, still with his back to the camera, imperturbable.* And do you expect to return often to the ' Funambules '?

GARANCE : No, my friend, that is over. I shall not go back again!

COUNT : I am delighted. *He says this out of shot, the camera is on* GARANCE, *still at her dressing table.*

GARANCE : You shouldn't speak badly of the ' Funambules ', you forget that it was there that we met.

Long shot, with him in the centre of the room, and her still at her dressing table.

COUNT *sadly ironic* : And that, no doubt, is why, since our return, you make this pious pilgrimage every evening?

The COUNT *paces back and forth. Quick close shot of* GARANCE *in the mirror.*

GARANCE *simply* : No, my dear.

Long shot as the COUNT *sits down on the left of the frame, and as he taps down the tobacco in his pipe, he turns slightly towards* GARANCE, *motionless in front of her dressing table. (Still on page 185)*

COUNT : The opposite would have surprised me. *Hiding his irri-*

tation. Might I know, Garance, the name of the ' gentleman ' who was with you just now, and if it was with him that you spent the evening at the ' Funambules '?

GARANCE *medium close-up of her, backview, and her face in reflection*: The gentleman? . . . *Realising suddenly whom he is talking about* . . . Oh . . . I see. *Smiling.* It's just a boy I used to know came round to say hello.

COUNT : A very peculiar character, to use an understatement. What is he? . . . What does he do?

GARANCE *very simply*: He writes. But, to hide nothing from you, at the period when I knew him he was also a thief, and even, I believe, just a little bit of a murderer !

> *Close shot of the* COUNT, *sitting down, lighting his pipe.*

COUNT : I dare to hope, Garance, that there was nothing in the ' old days ', between you and this ' person '. *His voice anxious, and lower in tone.* You know that I have the most complete confidence in you.

GARANCE *close shot of her* : That does you no great credit because I've never had reason to lie to you.

COUNT : That's true, but all the same, I would be grateful if you saw people like that as little as possible. Actors, if necessary, one can accept . . . but thieves and murderers . . . it is a little shocking, don't you think?

> *Medium shot of* GARANCE *who, without replying to the* COUNT'S *question, gets up and goes to look for a jewel box on the centre table, the camera panning to follow her. Shot of her full face as she talks while putting her jewels into the box.*

GARANCE *dreamily* : Do you remember, my dear friend, that young Scotsman you provoked to a duel in Edinburgh, last year?

COUNT *off, very simply* : Yes, I remember very well — why?

GARANCE *turning towards the* COUNT : That young man was not nearly as good a shot as you, was he?

> *General shot: the* COUNT *in the foreground, three-quarters backview;* GARANCE *standing, facing the camera in the centre of the room, in front of the centre table.*

COUNT : Of course not ! And everybody knew it.

GARANCE : But you killed him just the same.

COUNT : An affair of honour, Garance !

GARANCE : All that because I smiled at him !

COUNT: Yes, in public, and several times.

GARANCE: But I told you that when I was smiling at him I was thinking of someone else!

Close shot of the COUNT: *he gets up and goes over to her out of shot. The camera pans to follow him.*

COUNT: Garance, try to understand me! I want so much for you to love me.

Close shot of the two of them: he kisses her hand.

GARANCE *murmuring*: For yourself . . .

COUNT: Oh, please, Garance, don't torment me. You know how much I love you and what I am capable of doing for you, because of you.

GARANCE *very sad*: Because of me.

She moves a few steps away, the camera tracking backwards to keep her in medium long shot.

COUNT: I love you Garance, as no other man . . .

GARANCE *interrupting*: . . . could ever love me! *She turns round to look at him.* So what are you complaining about?

She leaves him and moves out of shot. The COUNT, *full face, watches her move away.*

COUNT *pathetic*: I want you to love me.

Medium close-up of GARANCE, *seen from the back, but full face in reflection. She is back at her dressing table.*

GARANCE *weary*: But I do love you, my friend. You are charming, you are rich, you are witty, your friends admire you and others fear you, women find you very attractive . . . in fact everyone loves you, Edward. Really, I would have to be very difficult to please if I couldn't do as everybody else does!

Close shot of the COUNT, *full face, in the centre of the room. He remains motionless, slightly hunched, head lowered, and features twisted.*

COUNT: Be quiet, Garance. You know very well what I want . . . what I desire.

Medium close-up of GARANCE, *backview, the reflection of her face half hidden.*

GARANCE: You are extraordinary, Edward. Not only are you rich, but you want to be loved ' as if you were poor '! *She looks at the* COUNT. And what about the poor? Be reasonable, my friend, you can't take everything away from the poor!

Medium close-up of the COUNT, *full face.*

COUNT *more and more pathetic*: Garance, understand me!

GARANCE *long shot*: I understand you, Edward, and I have always done, and I shall continue to do all I can to be agreeable to you. But don't ask the impossible of me. However, if you wish . . . *A pause. She turns round and stands facing the* COUNT, *who is slightly out of frame.* If it would please you, tomorrow the whole of Paris shall know not only that I love you, but that I am crazy about you!

> *Medium close-up of the* COUNT *who looks wretchedly at* GARANCE *without saying anything. Then cut back to* GARANCE *in close shot.*

GARANCE: Yes, crazy about you! I'll tell everybody. I'll shout it from the rooftops. But to you . . . to you alone, my friend, I will tell you this: I have loved a man, and I love him still. I came to Paris to see him again. He sent a message to say that he had forgotten me . . . and now I have only one idea, to go away . . . to go away.

> *Fade out.*
> *It is night time on the* 'Boulevard du Temple'. *Long shot of the* 'Boulevard' *aimed towards the façade of the* 'Funambules'. *Crowds pass by. Medium shot of the passers-by who glance at some posters on which can be read:*

BAPTISTE DEBUREAU
in
The Rag and Bone Man

All the posters are plastered across with streamers on which can be read 'No Performance'.

It is day. The corridor of the first floor of the 'Hotel du Grand Relais'. MME HERMINE *comes up the stairs carrying a light meal on a tray. She starts down and stops by the door to the room which* GARANCE *used to have, knocks, and listens.*

VOICE OFF *from inside the room*: Come in!

> *Inside the room, medium shot of* MME. HERMINE *as she comes in and closes the door.*

MME. HERMINE: Here's your dinner, Monsieur Baptiste.

> *Medium shot of* BAPTISTE, *slightly high angle. He is lying on his side on the bed, face to the wall, back to the camera.*

BAPTISTE *murmuring*: Thank you, Madame Hermine, but I'm

not very hungry.

Cut back to MME. HERMINE, *the camera pans to follow her as she carries the tray over to the table.*

MME. HERMINE *shaking her head* : Oh, you're being unreasonable.

Cut back to BAPTISTE *who turns round, calmly agreeing.*

BAPTISTE : It's true. I'm being unreasonable!

MME. HERMINE *puts the tray down on a table in the centre of the room and comes up to the bed with the camera panning to follow her.*

MME. HERMINE : But all the same, fancy staying here, hidden, cloistered like a monk!

Shot of the two of them, favouring BAPTISTE *who is lying on his back, his hands behind his head.*

BAPTISTE : Oh, no, monks pray. I only sleep, and dream.

MME. HERMINE : And all the time the whole world is looking for you.

BAPTISTE *sad* : The whole world. That's exaggerating a little.

MME. HERMINE : After all, think of it : the 'Funambules' is closed . . . and your wife, your little boy, your father, the whole company, you can't have forgotten them all just like that!

She comes back to the centre of the room in medium long shot, and lays out the meal. Cut back to him in medium close-up, sitting on the side of the bed.

BAPTISTE : No. I couldn't go on living like that! . . . like a lunatic in an asylum, and everyone around you talks in low voices, 'What's the matter with him? Is he ill?' Ah! When I think that to please them I even had to go and see a doctor!

MME. HERMINE *as she goes on laying the table* : And what did he say?

BAPTISTE *high angle shot, he smiles bitterly* : Oh, he told me that I was as fit as a fiddle . . . *imitating the doctor* . . . 'A little bit of depression, a little bit of overwork, three times nothing!' . . . And to round it off : 'No medicine, but some good advice — go and see Baptiste, it'll take you out of yourself.' *Dreamy again, then anxious* . . . and what if I don't want to be taken out of myself?

Medium long shot: he is half out of shot in the foreground, she is standing by the table.

BAPTISTE *abruptly* : What day is it?

MME. HERMINE : Thursday.

BAPTISTE *horrified* : Thursday!

MME. HERMINE : Oh, do you know, this evening it's the first night of ' Othello ', at the ' Grand Theatre ', with Monsieur Frederick. You should go, it'd take you out of yourself. *Realising.* Oh! . . . sorry!

Close shot, then medium shot of BAPTISTE, *facing the camera, sitting on the bed.*

BAPTISTE *dreamily* : One could make a nice pantomime out of ' Othello '. *With a bitter smile.* A man who kills his love, and dies of it. *He gets up and goes over towards her, the camera panning to follow him.* Poor man! . . . *Shot of the two of them, him facing the camera, and her backview in the foreground* . . . a sad and ridiculous story, like so many others, like mine or yours, Madame Hermine, who waste your empty days here with your poor heart empty too . . .

MME. HERMINE : Oh, Monsieur Baptiste!

Close shot of BAPTISTE *who walks up and down, and comes back towards the bed which he stares at.*

BAPTISTE : Ah! Yes, it's all sad and ridiculous, like me! *He sits on the bed, very weary.* Like me. I was here, years ago, here, by this bed, in this room! And she was there too, standing, smiling, happy and lovely in the freshness of the night. And she said ' How simple love is! '

He stands up, shaking his fists in the air, unable to bear it, and starts to walk up and down the room again, the camera panning to follow him.

BAPTISTE *desperate and almost weeping* : And I, I didn't listen to her! I didn't take her in my arms! No — I made conditions: ' Do you love me as I love you? ' And I shut the door, that door there, for ever between me and my love!

Medium shot of MME. HERMINE *who stares at* BAPTISTE *with compassion, astonished and moved. Cut back to* BAPTISTE *who suddenly becomes aware of the presence of* MME. HERMINE.

BAPTISTE *violent* : What are you doing there? *Quick cut back to her, surprised.* I'm talking to myself. You hear what I say, but I'm not really talking to you.

MME. HERMINE *medium reverse angle shot of her* : Oh! . . . *Very upset.* Monsieur Baptiste!

He comes over to her. Shot of the two of them, side by side, next to the table laden with food.

BAPTISTE : Oh, Madame Hermine, forgive me, I didn't mean to be unkind. It's true you have been the greatest help to me, and you've been so discreet!

MME. HERMINE : But of course, it's only natural!

She goes out. The camera stays on BAPTISTE. *Left alone, he goes over to the window, then begins to walk about again.*

BAPTISTE *more and more feverish* : Oh! I can't bear it, I can't stay here any longer, alone. I must go out, I must walk!

On the ground floor of the hotel, MME. HERMINE *is coming down the staircase which leads into the courtyard, with a lamp in her hand. The camera pans and tracks to follow her. She comes towards* NATALIE *who is on the threshold of her office. Medium shot of the two of them.*

NATALIE *very simply* : Well, Madame Hermine, has he eaten?

MME. HERMINE : He's just going to.

NATALIE : That's good. *Changing tone.* I'm very grateful to you for telling me where he was. I was so worried.

MME. HERMINE : It was the very least one woman could do for another.

NATALIE *medium close-up, full face,* MME. HERMINE *half out of shot* : He needs solitude. We must leave him alone. You see he's not an ordinary sort of man . . . [he's so sensitive, always dreaming impossible dreams.] (Cut in the final editing.)

MME. HERMINE *embarrassed* : Of course.

Close shot of the two of them.

NATALIE *very gentle* : You know, sleepwalkers who walk on roofs, if you call them, they fall down. Baptiste is like them. We musn't call him, we must leave him, and wait until he is calm, until he wakes up. *Smiling and sure of herself.* And when he wakes up he will come back!

Fade out.

It is night on the ' Boulevard du Temple '. Long shot favouring the top of the façade of the ' Grand Theatre ', then pan to the bottom to frame the crowd who are pressing round the brightly lit entrance. Cabs pass on with difficulty after having dropped off couples in evening dress. The posters can hardly be seen in the crowd.

In the auditorium of the ' Grand Theatre ', *quick shot of the audience in the Gods, rapt and absorbed, then long high angle shot of the packed house. When the stage can be made out in the background the décor is seen to represent the exterior towers of a castle.* OTHELLO *and* IAGO *are in the centre of the stage.* OTHELLO (FREDERICK, *with his face painted black) prowls nervously to and fro in front of* IAGO *who is standing motionless.*

OTHELLO (FREDERICK) *partially off screen* : Get me some poison, Iago — this night. I'll not expostulate with her, lest her body and beauty unprovide my mind again — this night, Iago. *Crane shot from in front to frame the scene in medium long shot.*

IAGO : Do it not with poison; strangle her in her bed, even the bed she has contaminated.

Reverse angle shot: the auditorium seen from the stage, particularly the stalls; the camera tracks forward to frame in medium shot a very attentive spectator. It is LACENAIRE.

OTHELLO : Ay, let her rot and perish, and be damned tonight. (In the actual play this line comes before the previous dialogue, but this order must have been dictated by the exigencies of the editing.)

Cut back to long shot of the stage where OTHELLO *angrily prowls to and fro in front of* IAGO. *The camera makes a semicircular pan to end on a box, and tracks forward to frame it in close shot:* GARANCE *and the* COUNT *are sitting side by side facing the camera.* GARANCE *is watching the stage, which is out of shot, through a pair of opera glasses. The* COUNT, *always phlegmatic, puts his hand in front of his mouth discreetly, with an affected air of boredom.*

The camera remains on this couple who speak while the play can be heard off.

COUNT: This debased violence, this lack of decorum . . no really, I cannot say that I appreciate this Monsieur Shakespeare. *Looking at* GARANCE. Though it's true that one no longer goes to the theatre to listen to a play, but rather to ' see the actors '.

OTHELLO *off* : . . . for she shall not live. No, my heart is turned to stone : I strike it, and it hurts my hand. O, the world hath not a sweeter creature. She might lie by an Emperor's side and command him tasks.

IAGO *off* : Nay, that's not your way.

GARANCE: Do not forget, my friend, that it was you who insisted on coming.

COUNT: No doubt I had my reasons.

Long shot of the stage seen from the box, slightly high angle: OTHELLO suddenly comes forward as close as possible to the box and indirectly addresses himself to GARANCE.

OTHELLO: The pity of it, Iago! Oh! Iago! . . . *quick shot of GARANCE in close shot, looking at him through the opera glasses; quick shot of the COUNT; quick shot of FREDERICK repeating . . .* the pity of it! . . .

Cut back to a close shot of the box; the COUNT stares at GARANCE; a series of close shots of her watching the stage, and him staring at her, anxious, but trying not to show it. Cut to LACENAIRE in the audience, very happy. Cut back to GARANCE and the COUNT facing the camera in their box, when someone knocks at the door of the box.

COUNT *turning round*: Come in!

Two little negroes, wearing sumptuous stage costumes, put down a huge basket of flowers, and go away, shutting the door behind them. (Still on page 185) The COUNT looks at GARANCE who, smiling, and impassive, picks up a note pinned to the flowers, and is about to read it when he holds out his hand.

COUNT: May I, Garance?

GARANCE *shrugging her shoulders*: Of course.

She holds the note out to him. Shot of the COUNT full face, and GARANCE half out of shot.

COUNT *reading*: 'Desdemona has come this evening. Othello is no longer jealous. Othello is cured. Thank you.'

He looks at GARANCE with an expression of cruelty.

GARANCE *very calm*: But no

OTHELLO: Hang her! I do but say what she is.

OTHELLO: Had it pleased Heaven to try me with affliction; had they rained All kinds of sores and shames on my bare head, Steep'd me in poverty to the very lips, Given to captivity me and my utmost hopes, I should have found in some place of my soul A drop of patience; but alas, to make me A fixed finger for the time of scorn my friend. I assure you that you are deceiving yourself.

COUNT *icy*: Of course, Garance, it is I who am ' deceiving myself ', and you play no part in it. *Pointing to the stage.* Nor Othello. *Abruptly pleading.* I beg you, Garance, tell me the truth. Is it him?

To point his slow unmoving
   finger at — O, O!
Yet I could bear that too; well,
   very well:
But there where I have
   garner'd up my heart,
Where either I must live, or
   bear no life,
The fountain from the which
   my current runs,
Or else dries up — to be
   discarded thence!
Or keep it as a cistern for foul
   toads
To knot and gender in!

GARANCE *exasperated*: No, my friend, it is not him.
   Dissolve.
   It is night on the ' Boulevard du Temple '. *Medium long tracking shot of the façade of the* ' Grand Theatre ', *and across the poster. Insert shot of the poster.*

' THIS EVENING, FIRST NIGHT
FREDERICK LEMAITRE
in
OTHELLO
after the play by William Shakespeare '

Although it is brightly lit up, the façade and the pavement are almost empty now, because the show has already begun. The camera pans to frame on one side the cab drivers who are eating and drinking. A passer-by comes up to the group. The camera follows him. It is BAPTISTE. *He seems to be walking in a dream, without hurrying, staring straight ahead of him, like a sleepwalker. He stops, hesitates for a moment, and then goes into the theatre. The camera retraces the previous pan across the poster to follow him, and in the background* BAPTISTE *can be seen by the box office shaking the hand of the* FRONT OF HOUSE MANAGER, *who points in to the auditorium. Inside the* ' Grand Theatre ', *a general shot, with the stage in the foreground and the auditorium in the background. The décor represents* DESDEMONA'S *bedroom.* OTHELLO *walks over to the bed where* DESDEMONA *is lying.*

OTHELLO: That handkerchief which I so loved and gave thee,
    Thou gav'st to Cassio.

DESDEMONA: No, by my life and soul!
    Send for the man and ask him.

OTHELLO: Sweet soul, take heed,
    Take heed of perjury: thou art on thy death-bed.

Medium close-up of GARANCE *and the* COUNT *facing the camera in their box. The scene can be heard continuing off.*

COUNT *icy*: To die, it's quickly said.

COUNT: But it's done even more quickly.

GARANCE: Why are you laughing, my friend?

COUNT: Quite simply because I am thinking that if we fight tomorrow morning, this actor will not be here tomorrow evening to talk about death.

GARANCE: Edward, you must be mad!

COUNT: Why should it matter to you since he is not the man you love?

DESDEMONA *off*: Ay, but not yet to die.

OTHELLO: Yes, presently.
Therefore confess thee freely
    of thy sin;
For to deny each article with
    oath
Cannot remove nor choke
    the strong conception
That I do groan withal.
    Thou art to die.

DESDEMONA: Kill me tomorrow: let me live tonight!

OTHELLO: Nay, if you strive . . .

DESDEMONA: But half an hour!

    GARANCE *takes her opera glasses and looks at the stage. Close shot of the stage as seen by her, then medium long shot of the stage from the auditorium:* OTHELLO *has taken* DESDEMONA *by the shoulders.*

OTHELLO: Being done, there is no pause.

DESDEMONA: But while I say one prayer!

OTHELLO: It is too late.

    He takes her by the throat and strangles her. (Still on page

186) *Medium shot, then general shot with the stage in the background as the curtain falls, while the spectators stand up and applaud enthusiastically. Several long and medium shots of the cheering audience.*
High angle medium long shot of the box where GARANCE *and the* COUNT *are sitting. The* COUNT *gets up, and* GARANCE *follows suit.*
[*Medium shot of* AVRIL *sitting alone in the Gods. Among all the people clapping he is weeping for poor Desdemona.*]
(Cut in the editing.)
Slightly high angle medium shot of BAPTISTE *near a column on one of the balconies. He shudders and pales as he sees: high angle shot, following his line of vision, of* GARANCE *and the* COUNT *leaving their box. Loud applause can be heard off. Cut back to* BAPTISTE, *who although he is overwhelmed by the sight of* GARANCE, *does not forget to clap as he walks out of shot.*

VOICES *off* : Bravo ! Bravo ! Bravo Frederick !
Slightly high angle general shot of a corridor behind the boxes. Great bustle, as a flood of people crushed against each other push towards the exit, while others struggle against the tide towards the Green Room.

VOICES IN THE CROWD : Frederick really surpassed himself this time . . . Mind out, I have got feet you know . . . Didn't he look marvellous in that costume? . . . A splendid play, isn't it? . . . Oh, it's a fine play, but a bit sad . . .
Medium shot, slightly high angle, of the spectators. They are moving slowly from right to left. A couple of dandies are trying to go in the opposite direction.

AN OLD MAN : That's not the way out !
FIRST DANDY : We're not going out, we're going backstage.
The camera tracks backwards to frame GARANCE *and the* COUNT *who are walking towards it.*

COUNT : Don't persist, Garance. I have a great desire to congratulate this extraordinary actor.
GARANCE : If you do it, Edward, I will never see you again.
COUNT *sarcastic* : And for the same reason, you will never see him again either !
Close shot: the COUNT *leaves the shot, and the camera*

remains on GARANCE, *motionless and furious. A pause, then suddenly a quick shot of* BAPTISTE *a few yards away.*

BAPTISTE *in a low voice* : Garance!

Cut back to GARANCE, *who, without really hearing the voice, automatically turns her head towards* BAPTISTE, *who is out of shot. Close shot of her, astonished and overwhelmed, unable to believe her eyes.*

GARANCE *also in a low voice, her eyes shining with happiness*: Baptiste!

Close shot of BAPTISTE, *and the camera pans to follow him as he moves towards* GARANCE. *He takes her arm.*

BAPTISTE : Come!

GARANCE : Where?

BAPTISTE *so moved that he does not know what to reply* : Oh! . . . I don't know where! . . . it doesn't matter where!

GARANCE allows him to lead her away. The camera pans to follow them. They go out of shot as the camera reveals LACENAIRE *in close shot, alone, in the middle of the crowd; he has watched the meeting, motionless and smiling in a peculiar way.*

Backstage, the Green Room is very brilliantly lit. Friends who have come to congratulate the actors, pretty women and society people have formed themselves into groups. The camera pans over the whole scene, with a slightly high angle crane shot, tracking to frame in medium shot a group round FREDERICK LEMAITRE. *He is standing to the right of a long curtain drawn over a window which opens onto the balcony. The* COUNT *is talking to* FREDERICK *with contained violence, in a polite tone that is both menacing and affected. Beside him are* GEORGE, *a friend of the* COUNT'S *and another friend. The conversation is filmed in a series of reverse angle shots framing whoever is talking in close-up facing the camera, with the others beside him or half out of the picture.*

COUNT : Absolutely, Monsieur; you played the part of this simple-minded and blood-thirsty brute as if you found it perfectly natural.

FREDERICK *smiling* : You are too kind, Monsieur, but I hope that above all I played it as Shakespeare wrote it — as if it was the most natural thing in the world!

COUNT *still mocking* : A very peculiar character, this ' Monsieur

Shakespeare'! I have been given to understand that he served his literary apprenticeship . . . *More and more contemptuous* . . . chopping meat on a butcher's slab.

FREDERICK *still smiling*: And why not?

COUNT *continuing*: Which would explain the bestial and savage character of his plays, and why, when he was alive, he was a great favourite among such people as dockers, carters . . .

FREDERICK *interrupting ironically*: And kings!

GEORGE *interrupting in turn, in a very affected voice*: Ah! . . . Well, now I understand why the play 'dis-pleased' me . . . 'shocked' me. *Smiling*. Tomorrow evening I will take a seat for my coachman. *The others laugh*. It would be an interesting experiment, don't you agree?

FREDERICK *sure of himself*: I hope you will allow me the pleasure of offering you a box for your horses . . . *A pause, then imitating the dandy's voice* . . . It would be an 'interesting experiment', don't you agree?

> *On the Balcony of the* 'Grand Theatre'. *It is lit by the moon, and also by the lights of the Green Room filtering through the drawn curtains. The Balcony stretches away from the camera. In the centre* GARANCE *and* BAPTISTE, *holding each other closely, are talking in low voices. Medium shot of both of them, she is three-quarters backview, and he is facing the camera.*

GARANCE *her eyes shining with happiness**: And I thought you didn't want to see me again!

BAPTISTE: And I thought I had lost you for ever!

> *Series of reverse angle shots in close-up of whoever is speaking, the other being backview and half out of shot.*

GARANCE: I never forgot you. You have helped me to live through all these years. It's you who have prevented me from becoming old, and stupid, and spoiled.

BAPTISTE: I've thought of you every day.

GARANCE: My life was so empty, and I felt so alone! But I told myself 'you have no right to be sad, you are one of the happy ones in spite of everything, because someone really loved you.'

BAPTISTE, GARANCE'S *hand caresses his cheek*: And I still love you. I have never stopped loving you. And you, Garance? Do you love

---

* In the script; her eyes cannot actually be seen until the next shot.

201

me? *But he stops himself abruptly and seizes* GARANCE'S *hand.* No, don't tell me. I demand nothing. You are here, that's the only thing that matters. Yes, you are here, alive, in my arms, as you were the first time!

GARANCE *close-up* : All I want is to have you in my arms, and for your eyes to look into me, and your lips to . . . kiss me!

Medium long shot of the balcony, and the couple embracing . . . pan towards a window: LACENAIRE *watches, with his ambiguous smile. The camera follows* LACENAIRE *as he leaves the window, and still smiling, he walks through the various groups towards the camera, which tracks backwards in front of him and then pans as he approaches the group comprising the* COUNT, FREDERICK, GEORGE *and another* DANDY.

LACENAIRE *very much at ease* : Congratulations, Frederick. A remarkable performance!

FREDERICK *gesturing towards* LACENAIRE : Gentlemen, may I introduce . . .

COUNT *with brutal insolence* : No need . . . *To the others* . . . I have already met this person once, and that was once too often!

FREDERICK : Now isn't that funny. *To* LACENAIRE. Just imagine for quite some time these gentlemen have been trying to insult me . . . very politely, of course.

LACENAIRE : We all have to find some way of passing the time.

FREDERICK *still very polite, to the* COUNT : Gentlemen, I assure you, you are wrong not to appreciate my friend Pierre-François. I haven't known him very long, but I assure you that, in his own fashion, he's a remarkable fellow . . . LACENAIRE *bows, amused and delighted* . . . and possessed of no mean talent!

COUNT *more and more insolent* : All the talents, I've no doubt.

LACENAIRE *modest* : It takes all kinds to make the world . . . *Little laugh* . . . or to destroy it!*

GEORGE : Quite good . . . only a pun, but quite good.

ANOTHER : Most amusing!

COUNT : Really? You find this creature amusing? *Pointing contemptuously at* LACENAIRE. Well, let's amuse ourselves! I can assure you that we run absolutely no risk. This gentleman does not fight duels.

---

* Translator's Note : A pun on ' faire ' and ' défaire '.

LACENAIRE *smiling* : Absolutely not.

COUNT : Might one be permitted to ask, my friend, how you are utilising your talents at the moment?

LACENAIRE *alone in close-up, very insolent* : If you are interested! *Very serious.* I am completing . . . I'm just about to put the finishing touches to something quite fascinating, which will be a resounding success.

COUNT *close shot, ironic* : A tragedy, of course?

LACENAIRE *very close shot* : No, a comedy, a farce . . . or call it a tragedy if you prefer . . . why not? It's exactly the same . . . doesn't make any difference. *In an insulting tone, to the* COUNT *who is out of shot* . . . or very little difference. For instance : when a king is deceived it's a tragedy, a drama of faithfulness. *He laughs.* It's not his wife who betrays him ! . . .

FREDERICK *amused* : No, it's Fate !

LACENAIRE : Yes, Fate. *Close-up of the* COUNT *silent, and cut back to close-up of* LACENAIRE. But when we're dealing with a poor devil like you or I, Monsieur de Monteray, and when I say ' I ', it's just a figure of speech, then it's no longer a tragedy . . . it's a music hall joke, the pathetic tale of a cuckold.

> *Quick shot of the* COUNT *frowning, then medium shot of* FREDERICK *and* LACENAIRE.

FREDERICK *going one better, amused and lyrical* : And yet it's the same wood beneath the poor man's hat and the king's crown. *More and more lyrical.* The dead wood of love which rots under the skulls of those who are not loved !

> *Quick shot of the* COUNT, *pale and dumb, and cut back to medium shot of* LACENAIRE *and* FREDERICK.

LACENAIRE : Always the same wood, the same stories, the same tears. *Smiling.* So in the end, gentlemen, it really doesn't matter what type of play my little piece is, the important thing is that it should be amusing, and that the author should be the first to laugh at it !

> *Medium shot of the group.*

GEORGE *sarcastic* : If it's put on.

LACENAIRE : Don't worry, Monsieur, it will be put on. I can even say it's already being played, . . . and if you'd like parts . . .

GEORGE : Oh, very droll !

LACENAIRE *close shot* : Yes, it's rather amusing. But I warn you that there are murders in it, and that when the curtain falls, the dead won't get up to take a bow!

COUNT *medium shot of him and his friends*: This creature is becoming intolerably boring. Shall we throw him out?

Close shot of LACENAIRE *shaking his head with disturbing, tranquil assurance, while the* COUNT'S *two friends throw themselves on him.*

LACENAIRE: I assure you, Monsieur, that you will be making a mistake if you try to humiliate me. Anyway, you won't be able to. *Dreamy and smiling.* I'm not a character out of a bedroom farce, whereas you are . . .

[*The* COUNT, *irritated beyond endurance, points to* LACENAIRE *and says to his friends.*

COUNT: Please, gentlemen, get rid of him.] (Cut during the shooting to give the scene more punch.)

Medium shot of LACENAIRE. *The camera follows him slowly to enlarge its field of vision as he pushes the* COUNT's *friends aside, approaches the curtained window giving onto the balcony, and seizes the curtain cord.*

LACENAIRE: And I'll prove it!

He draws back the curtain, revealing GARANCE *and* BAPTISTE, *embracing on the balcony.* (*Still on page 186*) *Surprised by the sudden light they look towards the window and move slightly apart. Close shot of the* COUNT, *paralysed and speechless. Shot of the window. Shot of* LACENAIRE *laughing. Close shot of the* COUNT. *Medium shot of the group, three-quarters back view, with the window in the background. They all seem embarrassed. In front of the window,* LACENAIRE *is still smiling;* FREDERICK, *beside himself with anger and disgust, moves menacingly towards him.*

FREDERICK *to* LACENAIRE: What you have just done . . .

But the COUNT *arriving in his turn hurriedly pulls the curtains shut and seizes* FREDERICK.

COUNT: Has nothing to do with you!

The two men try to outstare each other. LACENAIRE, *obviously delighted with his coup de théâtre, starts to laugh out loud.*

LACENAIRE: Gentlemen, I have just tasted one of the rarest moments of a lifetime.

The camera pans to follow him as he leaves, walking back-

wards, but with dignity, and to the great astonishment of the women in the room, who understand nothing about what has been going on, calls to the COUNT.

LACENAIRE : So much the worse for you, Edward de Monteray! I have warned you that I am not the sort of man you can throw out with impunity!

The COUNT'S *two friends approach* LACENAIRE. *He looks them up and down, smiles, and moves away. The two men follow him. The camera pans back to a close shot of* FREDERICK *and the* COUNT.

COUNT : I regret to inform you again, Monsieur, that what has just taken place is no business of yours.

FREDERICK : How do you know? Jealousy belongs to everyone . . . even if women belong to no one!

On the balcony GARANCE *and* BAPTISTE *in very close shot; she facing the camera, and him in the foreground, three-quarters view.*

GARANCE : They're going to fight a duel!

BAPTISTE : Because of us.

GARANCE *very gently* : No, because of me. *They put their arms round each other.* But they won't fight before tomorrow.

BAPTISTE : No?

GARANCE *in a low voice* : No . . . we have the night in front of us, with us . . . for us . . .

Fade out.

In the Green Room, close shot of FREDERICK *and the* COUNT *face to face. The* COUNT *holds out his card to* FREDERICK.

COUNT *very calm* : And if I am not at home, I shall be in the Turkish Baths, where I hope to have the pleasure of entertaining . . .

FREDERICK *taking the card and interrupting him* : . . . two of my friends. *He bows slightly and ironically.* Believe me, Monsieur, I am deeply flattered that you wish to do me the honour of despatching to the next world a man who does not belong to your society in this one!

With debonair grace, he makes a splendidly theatrical exit, turning round, with the camera panning to follow him in long shot, as he cleaves his way through the crowd under the admiring glances of several pretty women. He climbs a grand

staircase, salutes the people coming down, and disappears.
Dissolve.
Long shot of a corridor in the 'Grand Theatre' *leading towards*
one of the exits. LACENAIRE *comes towards the camera, very*
relaxed. The camera tracks backwards to the theatre entrance
where AVRIL *is waiting for him. Shot of the two men.* AVRIL,
who was squatting on his heels, gets up and they both walk
along, talking, with the camera tracking backwards beside
them: AVRIL *three-quarters back view, and* LACENAIRE *facing*
the camera in tight close shot.
[LACENAIRE : Avril, you see before you a man who has just been
thrown out on his ear . . . with absolutely no discretion.
AVRIL *horrified* : Oh! Monsieur Lacenaire . . . they did that to
you?
LACENAIRE *playing with his cane, very much the dandy* : Yes, I
assure you. But I regret nothing! When I think that these fine
gentlemen will probably cut each other's throats tomorrow morning . . . for a woman . . . and because of me . . . really, it warms
my heart. *He puts on his hat.*
AVRIL *happy* : A duel? . . . Are we going to be seconds?
LACENAIRE : No, this time I don't suppose they'll ask us . . .
AVRIL : Pity! I love duels!
LACENAIRE : Perhaps we could arrange something; anyway, if
you aren't witness to a duel there's quite a good chance that you'll
witness something else. *A pause.* Because, if you come to think
about it, as far as honour is concerned, it's me, Lacenaire, who's
been insulted . . . Yes, yes, insulted, offended, even humiliated,
because they threw me out, ignominiously!
AVRIL : Oh! Monsieur Lacenaire! . . . Fancy doing that to you!
Cut as they go out of shot.]*
It is night, in GARANCE'S *room at the* ' Hotel Relais '. *Medium*
long shot of the door opening. GARANCE *and* BAPTISTE *come*
into the room, and the camera pans round to look at it.
GARANCE *goes over towards the window, which is open, and*
full of moonlight . . . then, full of emotion, turns round to-
wards BAPTISTE.
GARANCE : How beautiful the moonlight is. Look, Baptiste, it's

---

*This scene was not in any version of the script, but must have been
improvised during the shooting.

shining for us like it shone that first evening.

She leans towards the window. Shot of the room seen from outside.

GARANCE *at the window*: . . . and the window's wide open, like it was that first evening.

She turns round again to BAPTISTE. *Shot from inside the room of* GARANCE *facing the camera in medium shot; the camera pans to follow her as she goes over to* BAPTISTE.

GARANCE: It's wonderful! Everything is the same; nothing has changed!

She approaches the table: they are face to face, separated by the table.

GARANCE: The table is still in the same place! *Then she turns towards the bed.* There's the bed I used to sleep on! . . .

BAPTISTE *comes over to her and takes her in his arms.*

BAPTISTE: You haven't changed either, Garance. There's still the same sweetness in your voice, the same light in your eyes . . .

GARANCE *very low*: . . . a very little light!

BAPTISTE: And your heart beating under my hand . . .

GARANCE: Baptiste!

BAPTISTE: You were right, Garance, love is so simple.

They are pressed closely together, and sway gently sideways to sit down on the bed, as the camera pans towards the open window.

GARANCE *off*: Yes, when you love each other!

Fade out.

It is daytime on the 'Boulevard du Temple'. *Shot of the Pierrot representing* BAPTISTE *on the façade of the* 'Funambules', *with the streamer advertising* 'The Rag and Bone Man, Pantomime in four scenes by M. Cot d'Ordan'.

The camera pans with background street noises, very gay, to a high angle long shot of the street. It is carnival time. Most of the people in the street — at first there are not very many, but the number continually increases — are disguised in fancy dress and masked, some of them in very pretty costumes; but others are dressed in what used to be called mummers' costumes. They chase each other along the street, shouting, singing and playing jokes, blowing trumpets, and pinching women or forcibly embracing them. Other, luckier ones, piled into carriages with pretty girls, embrace them, make animal noises, or start violent confetti battles with pedestrians. Pancake sellers installed under the trees with their trays, cry out to attract the passers-by:

PANCAKE SELLER : Pancakes, lovely pancakes!

Shrove Tuesday, Pancake day,

There's some for you, don't go away!

High angle medium long shot framing LACENAIRE *and* AVRIL *as they walk rapidly through the crowd, followed by the camera which is mounted on a crane. They are going towards the Turkish Baths.*

The interior of the Turkish Baths. The décor is very Eastern. Long shot of LACENAIRE *and* AVRIL *coming down a staircase, which is covered in mosaic like the walls. Faint oriental music can be heard in the background. The camera pans to follow them to a reception desk where an* ARAB *is dozing. Medium shot of the three of them, the* ARAB *stands up when he hears their footsteps.*

ARAB : A bath, gentlemen?

LACENAIRE : No, we would just like to have a word with the Count of Monteray.

ARAB : Now? But he's resting!

LACENAIRE *sharply* : He's expecting us.

The ARAB *looks carefully at* LACENAIRE *and* AVRIL. *He hesitates for a moment, then . . .*

ARAB : Well, in that case, if you'd like to follow me . . .

The ARAB *leaves his desk and leading the way, goes towards a large room which can be seen on the right.*

General shot, the camera tracking backwards, then sideways, following the ARAB *who leads* LACENAIRE *and* AVRIL *through the baths, where several people are lying recumbent, then past a closed swimming pool.* LACENAIRE *walks with a firm step, his smile more disturbing than ever, while* AVRIL *gives him an anxious look from time to time.* [*At the same time, perhaps to give himself courage,* AVRIL *hums his favourite tune.*] (In the script, but left out during the shooting.)

New shot of a corridor along which the three men are walking, back to the camera. Then medium shot in front of the door of a private bathroom. The ARAB *knocks, and then*

*goes in, pushing the door, which is a swing door without a
lock or latch. LACENAIRE and AVRIL wait in front of the
door. LACENAIRE gestures to AVRIL not to show himself
through the open door. Cut.*

*General shot of the bathroom, also decorated in oriental-style
mosaics: there is a little swimming pool hollowed out in the
floor, with steps leading down into it. The ARAB goes towards
a corner of the room where the COUNT is sitting on a divan,
wrapped in a bathrobe, reading a newspaper and smoking
a pipe.*

Medium shot of the two of them.

COUNT : What is it?

ARAB : Two gentlemen are asking for you. They say they are
expected.

COUNT : Two gentlemen? That's right. Let them come in.

*The ARAB bows and walks out of shot as the COUNT puts
down his newspaper and gets up. Medium long shot towards
the door: the COUNT, backview in the foreground, sees LACEN-
AIRE and AVRIL come in. (Still on page 187) Quick close shot
of the COUNT'S face, frightened in spite of his aristocratic
coldness. Cut back to the previous shot, but closer: LACENAIRE
comes forward, putting his hand inside his waistcoat ' over his
heart '. He walks out of frame as the camera zooms towards
AVRIL who is pressed against the wall, motionless, by the door,
his arms folded over his breast. He stares, his eyes popping,
at what is going on. At the first muffled groan off, he presses
himself even harder against the wall. There is the sound of a
body falling into the water. AVRIL jumps, then LACENAIRE
comes into shot — slight zoom backwards to frame them both
in tight close shot.*

AVRIL *admiring and terrified* : Oh! Monsieur Lacenaire!

LACENAIRE *very cold* : My poor Avril! *He pats his cheek, smiling.*
The play is over. You can go . . . *He moves towards the camera,
which frames him, alone, in close-up.* In fact, I'd advise you to go
and take a little rest in the country for a few weeks.

Close shot of AVRIL, full face, horrified, but also very anxious.

AVRIL *shattered* : And you?

LACENAIRE *he turns round dreamily, full of arrogant self-satisfac-
tion* : Oh, me . . . I shall stay here.

He indicates with a gesture to AVRIL *that he has no further need of anyone.*

LACENAIRE: After all a man like myself cannot decently be expected to run the risk of being executed by a provincial hangman. *A pause.* Absolutely not.

Close shot of AVRIL, *struck dumb. He stares at* LACENAIRE, *out of shot, then suddenly, stricken with terror, he shrinks back and runs away without waiting for anything more. Medium long shot of the doors, which are left swinging, after* AVRIL'S *departure; in the foreground, three-quarters back-view,* LACENAIRE *is standing motionless. Then he takes a few steps, the camera panning with him, to look in the pool, caressing his moustache. High angle close shot of the ground near the pool; in the foreground lies the* COUNT'S *pipe, broken on the mosaic floor, smoke still rising from it . . . A little above, the* COUNT'S *hand lies white and limp over the edge of the bath, from which steam is oozing . . . Close shot of the hand, and then cut back to* LACENAIRE *in medium long shot. Decisively, he walks over and pulls the cord of a bell, and sits down on the divan, peacefully, to wait. Fade out.*

*Outside in the '*Boulevard du Temple*', high angle general shot of the crowd, now very thick, dancing and waving. Confetti and streamers are being thrown down from windows. A group of* PIERROTS *are dancing in a chain, zig-zagging through the crowd. Various shots of the crowd and the* PIERROTS.

It is morning, GARANCE'S *room. Close shot of* BAPTISTE *lying dozing on the bed. Half-asleep still, he automatically feels the pillow beside his head. Suddenly realising that he is alone in the bed he wakes up and sits up in one movement. The camera tracks to reveal* GARANCE *standing in front of the mirror. She is dressed, and has just finished doing her hair. She turns round, and comes over to* BAPTISTE *as he sits on the bed.*

GARANCE: The night was so beautiful! But I must go. It would be too horrible if Frederick was killed because of me.

She sits down on the bed. Close shot of the two of them.

BAPTISTE: What are you going to do? *He takes her hand.*

GARANCE: I'll find Edward. I'll tell him that I was mad, that I

210

was stupid, and I'll beg him not to fight. (*Still on page 187*)

BAPTISTE : Will he listen to you?

GARANCE : Yes, if I tell him I love him, that I love only him.

BAPTISTE : You lie so badly, he'll never believe you!

GARANCE : Oh! He doesn't really care if it's true or not. *With a bitter smile.* I know him : all he really wants is for me to say it. *A pause.* In fact he doesn't really care if I love him, as long as I don't love anyone else. That's all his love is.

> *Close shot of the two of them, in profile.* BAPTISTE *puts an arm anxiously round her shoulders.*

BAPTISTE : And what if he asks you to go away with him?

GARANCE *very simply* : I'll go. *In a low voice.* And perhaps I'll come back. Whatever happens, I shall have to go some time.

BAPTISTE *crying out* : But why?

> *Close shot of the two of them.* GARANCE *is standing up.* BAPTISTE *leans his head against her breast.*

GARANCE *lowering her voice again, tenderly* : You know very well. *Very gently.* You have a very sweet little son, Baptiste.

BAPTISTE : Oh! Be quiet!

GARANCE : And you love your son. And your career, you love that too . . . and Natalie.

BAPTISTE : It's you that I love!

[BAPTISTE : Garance, it's you that I love, and no one else . . . and I won't be able to bear it if you go away.

> GARANCE, *deeply distressed, takes* BAPTISTE'S *head between her hands.*

GARANCE : And what about me, Baptiste? Do you think that I'll be able to bear it? . . . and I have no one but you!

> *Suddenly she kisses him, and hurries out of the room.*] (The ending was rewritten several times. In the final script, GARANCE left the hotel, and BAPTISTE pursued her through the crowd, without NATALIE appearing again. So the following scene must have been improvised during the shooting. Therefore the scene in square brackets was cut during the final editing to avoid repetition.)

General high angle shot of the crowd in the 'Boulevard du Temple', *near the* 'Hotel Grand Relais'. NATALIE *and her son are coming towards the hotel, the camera following them with a crane shot. Then the camera pans to pick them up in medium shot outside* MME. HERMINE'S *door.* NATALIE *is dressed in her best clothes, and holds the hand of little* BAPTISTE *who is dressed in a splendid Hussar costume.*

NATALIE *leaning down towards him* : Wait for me here and be good.

LITTLE BAPTISTE : Are you going to stay for long, mummy?

NATALIE : No, darling. Or if I do I'll come back for you.

LITTLE BAPTISTE : What are you going to do?

NATALIE : I can't tell you. It's a surprise.

She kisses the child on the cheek and goes out of frame. The camera stays for a moment on the boy.

Medium long shot of GARANCE'S *room.* GARANCE *is standing in the middle of the room, with her shawl over her shoulders, ready to go.* BAPTISTE *is also standing, in shirt sleeves, his hands behind his back. He paces nervously up and down, and comes over to her as she is putting on her gloves. They put their arms round each other.*

BAPTISTE : I won't let you leave me, do you hear, I can't bear it . . .

GARANCE : And what about me . . . I have nothing but you !

They are holding each other close when the camera pans to frame the door. A faint knocking can be heard.

In the corridor of the hotel, close shot of NATALIE *knocking at the door again. Hearing nothing she opens the door. The camera pans, then tracks slightly sideways to frame* NATALIE, *backview in the foreground holding open the door, and in the background* GARANCE *and* BAPTISTE *with their arms around each other. They move apart as the door opens, and look at her, without a word. Medium shot of* NATALIE, *standing on the threshold, astonished and distressed.*

NATALIE *almost mumbling* : I'm sorry, Baptiste, I just came . . . I thought I'd find you alone, all alone. *Quick shot of the couple and cut back to her.* Yes, you see it's the carnival, it's carnival day . . . the little one was so looking forward to it . . . that's why I came. He's dressed up as a Hussar, he's got a lovely Hussar's costume ! *Quick shot of the silent couple, and resume on* NATALIE. Oh, please don't leave me like this, all alone, it's so awful . . . *As she entreats him she speaks more easily, and does not stammer any more, gaining a little assurance.* Speak to me at least . . . answer me, say

212

something, it doesn't matter what, but . . . *Quick cut to the couple, still silent;* NATALIE *off.* Tell me to go away . . . *Shot of her again* . . . laugh if you like, but don't leave me like this!

Close shot of GARANCE *and* BAPTISTE, *very embarrassed and upset.*

BAPTISTE *not knowing what to say* : Natalie!

NATALIE *off* : Is that all you can say?

GARANCE *picks up the cape which she has put on a chair and comes towards* NATALIE *to go out. The camera pans in a semi-circle to follow her and frame* NATALIE, *who shuts the door to prevent* GARANCE *from leaving. Close shot of the two women face to face;* GARANCE *three-quarters backview in the foreground,* NATALIE *full face.*

NATALIE *almost shouting* : No!

GARANCE *reverse angle shot* : I assure you I must go.

NATALIE *close shot* : Again! . . . How easy it must be!

GARANCE *close shot* : What must be easy?

NATALIE *close shot* : Easy to go away . . . and then to come back. *Off, over a close shot of* GARANCE'S *sad face.* You go away, you are missed. Time works for you and you come back, all fresh, and made more beautiful by memory. *The camera is on* NATALIE *again.* Oh, yes, that must be easy! But to stay, and live with one man, to share with him the ordinary things of everyday life, that's something else. Yes, that's something else. *Shot of* GARANCE, NATALIE *continues off.* And you can do nothing against that. *On* NATALIE *again.* Six years, do you hear? Six years I've lived with him.

GARANCE *close shot; sad and dreamy, but deeply certain of what she is saying* : So have I.

NATALIE *dumbfounded* : You too?

GARANCE *close shot* : Yes, me too. Anywhere, everywhere, every day . . . and even at night, all the nights I spent with someone else, all those nights I was with him . . .

BAPTISTE *close shot; he seems to be very disturbed and embarrassed* : Garance!

Cut back to the two women in close shot; NATALIE *full face,* GARANCE *half out of shot, three-quarters back view.*

NATALIE : Let her go on, I want to know everything about you two. Yes, I want to know what is left for me . . . if you have left me enough to live on . . . And after all, what does it matter whether

213

you love him or not? You don't count . . . you don't exist for me.

NATALIE, the camera panning to follow her, passes in front of GARANCE. Medim shot of BAPTISTE three-quarters back-view, and NATALIE facing him. Entreating, she takes him by the shoulders.

NATALIE: Baptiste, listen to me, answer me; don't be afraid to make me suffer. Suffering's not very important, everybody does it. But I want to know, I want you to reply to me immediately, do you hear! Look at me; were you always thinking of her while you lived with me? Oh! You daren't even reply!

Medium long shot: discreetly GARANCE slips out, opening the door silently and closing it behind her.

NATALIE *return to the shot of her and* BAPTISTE: But you tell me a lot by keeping silent . . . and I understand . . . I understand what you don't say.

She shakes him gently. BAPTISTE turns his head and realises that GARANCE has gone.

BAPTISTE *shouting desperately*: Garance!

NATALIE holds him back, desperate, at the end of her tether. He brutally pulls himself free — medium long shot of the door — and rushes out following GARANCE.

BAPTISTE: Garance!

Cut back to medium shot of NATALIE, standing facing the camera in the centre of the room.

NATALIE *all her strength and confidence drained away*: Garance! . . . And me, Baptiste? What about me?

Cut.

It is daytime, a corner of the ' Boulevard du Temple ', seen in general shot, slightly high angle. It is much more crowded than before, there are more people moving about. Music, shouts and general hubbub of the street during carnival time can be heard. The camera slides across the crowd, and pans to reveal the façade of the ' Grand Relais Hotel '. GARANCE comes out and walks rapidly towards the Boulevard. Wide angle medium shot of the door of the ' Grand Relais '. After several seconds BAPTISTE also comes out and looks round for GARANCE. Through the noise he can just be heard shouting,

BAPTISTE: Garance, Garance!

Suddenly he starts and runs off after her. Reverse angle shot of him forcing his way through the crowd and desperately calling, ' Garance! '

BAPTISTE'S *son can just be seen as his father comes out of the hotel, dropping his trumpet and watching as his father disappears without even noticing him.* (This is not in the script, but visible in the film.)

BAPTISTE : Garance! Garance!

High angle medium shot, panning to follow BAPTISTE *as he loses himself in the crowd. Several shots of the passers-by, some of them dressed in the* PIERROT *costume that* BAPTISTE *has made famous. They laugh and bump into one another. One of them shouts to a friend.*

FIRST PIERROT : Hey, have you seen Baptiste?

(In the actual film this is almost inaudible, because Carné wanted to play down Baptiste's obsession with the Pierrot character, which was originally intended to play an important part in the plot — with the onstage murder of the Old Clothes Man.)

Close shot of BAPTISTE *swamped in the press of people, and trying to see over their heads. Medium long shot of* GARANCE *disappearing in the crowd while another group of* PIERROTS *confronts* BAPTISTE, *and holding each other round the waist in dance formation they bar his way.*

BAPTISTE *screaming* : Garance, Garance!

GARANCE *does not hear him and disappears in the crowd.* BAPTISTE *is seen in high angle medium shot and all around him, indifferent to his despair, the crowds laugh and dance. Suddenly the* OLD CLOTHES MAN *appears in shot, sniggering, reeling drunkenly on his feet and carrying several walking sticks and old umbrellas under his arm. He thrusts his way through to* BAPTISTE'S *side. During their conversation they both have to shout to make themselves heard above the noise of the crowd.*

OLD CLOTHES MAN *sniggering and imitating* BAPTISTE : Garance! BAPTISTE, *furious, stops and turns round as the* OLD CLOTHES MAN *takes him by the arm.*

BAPTISTE : Leave me alone.

OLD CLOTHES MAN *bursting out laughing* : Ah! Ah! Ah! . . . Garance! . . . Ah! . . . Ah! . . . Garance! . . . Come on Baptiste, don't make a fuss. You've had your fun, you can go home now.

Baptiste *trying in vain to wrench himself free* : Let me alone !

Old Clothes Man : You ought to be ashamed of yourself, yes, you should, true as I'm known as One to a bed, known as the Modest Maiden, the Bashful One, the Giver of Good Advice . . . because I've got a weakness for morality ! . . .

Baptiste *pulling himsef free*: Leave me alone, you disgust me ! . . .

Baptiste *goes on his way, but the* Old Man *pursues him, still sniggering. (Still on page 188)*

[Old Clothes Man : And what about her . . . she doesn't disgust you, does she ? Oh no, she is beauty, love, freshness !

Baptiste, *with the* Old Clothes Man *still beside him, manages with great difficulty to clear a way for himself, always searching for a glimpse of* Garance.

Old Clothes Man *shrieking* : What a world, what a filthy world, there's no morality . . . there's no more nothing . . . you're all corrupt, . . . depraved, good for nothing !

He waves his cane, furiously, and becomes more and more enraged, to the great amusement of the passers-by.

Old Clothes Man *furiously* : They should all be locked up, and whipped. *He catches* Baptiste *up and hangs onto his arm again.* Yes, you deserve to be flogged, you should both be flogged, you and your whore !

Suddenly Baptiste *stops. So does the camera. Close shot of* Baptiste *full face. Beside himself with anger and irritation he tears the walking stick out of the* Old Clothes Man's *hands, and holds it above his head. Close shot of the* Old Clothes Man. *Close shot of* Baptiste *striking him a violent blow on the head . . . close shot of the* Old Clothes Man *staggering under the blow, and collapsing among the feet of the crowd.* Baptiste, *free at last, disappears into the throng. Some of the passers-by form a circle round the* Old Clothes Man; *the camera frames him in high angle close shot, stretched out on the ground, surrounded by his cast-off clothes and old umbrellas. A thin trickle of blood comes from the wound on his forehead. He is dead. General shot of the crowd. Suddenly a woman cries out, and the people, seized with horror and fear, move away, forming a larger circle round the* Old Clothes Man *as he lies on the ground.*

High angle medium crane shot, followed by a medium long

shot, tracking backwards.
The crowd a little further on. BAPTISTE *comes in shot from the left, suddenly he sees . . .]**
Medium shot of GARANCE *who hails a cab and climbs into it. Cut back to* BAPTISTE *who hurls himself forward, thrusting his way through the crowd. He cries out a last time, lost in the crowd,*
BAPTISTE : Garance! Garance!
Cut back to GARANCE, *as seen by* BAPTISTE. *Without hearing, she gets into the carriage which immediately drives off. Slightly high angle medium shot of* BAPTISTE, *who tries to throw himself forward.*
BAPTISTE : Garance!
The camera tracks backwards, and frames him, swamped by the crowd. A group of PIERROTS *dance in a chain around him. [The group of* PIERROTS, *drunk, their faces painted white, form a barrier between* BAPTISTE *and the carriage. He struggles in vain to free himself.*
BAPTISTE : Let me through, let me through!

---

*(The part of the scene in square brackets was never shot. The whole scene, which was a particular favourite of Prévert's, was originally situated about three quarters of the way through the film, and Baptiste was arrested and tried. Marcel Carné left it out because it would have made the film too long, and also he wanted a less definitive ending to the film. The interesting thing is that this is based on historical fact, and was the story which particularly interested Barrault when he gave Carné the idea for the film. The original Debureau was going for a walk one day with his wife and two children when a young man bumped into him and started to insult him, shouting : ' Look at the Pierrot from the ' Funambules ' with his whore,' and calling him ' dummy, scarecrow '. Debureau got very angry, there was a fight, he hit the young man on the head with his cane, and he died in hospital an hour later. Debureau was arrested, and after being kept in prison for a month, was tried for manslaughter, and acquitted. The whole of Paris followed the story with passionate interest, and sympathy for Debureau; but after it was over he refused to play the Pierrot in Cot d'Ordan's pantomime, ' *Chand d'habits* ', because of the murder it contained.)

217

A DRUNKEN PIERROT : Have you seen Baptiste, Baptiste !

OTHERS TAKING UP THE CRY : Baptiste, Baptiste, have you seen Baptiste ?

Quick shot of GARANCE'S *carriage disappearing in the distance.*
PIERROTS : Have you seen Baptiste? . . . Baptiste. Have you seen Baptiste, Baptiste, Baptiste, Baptiste.

BAPTISTE, *in despair, hardly struggles to free himself any more.*] (The shouts of the Pierrots were all intended to fit with the obsession of Debureau/Baptiste with the Pierrot character, which fitted with the murder story, and are lost in the noise of the crowd in the film as it was finally shot.)

The hubbub and music rise to a crescendo over a shot of BAPTISTE *swamped in the crowd. Carriages pass by, filled with gay people and decorated with flowers. Confetti and streamers fall from above. Low angle shot of gay people in the windows of the buildings throwing them. General shot of the Boulevard, which is now being invaded by an enormous crowd, an indescribable hurly-burly of people, dominated by the white figures of hundreds of* PIERROTS, *who shout and laugh at one another, and sing and enjoy themselves. (Still on page 188)* BAPTISTE *has almost disappeared in the crush of people. He still cries out, but can no longer be heard.*

Medium shot of GARANCE, *facing the camera, sitting in a closed carriage, tossed and shaken by the movement of the horses. She is sad, and stares at the floor of the carriage with a vague, far away expression, lost and indifferent.*

Cut back to a medium high angle shot of BAPTISTE *swallowed up in the milling crowds, and then a general shot of the Boulevard in the midst of the carnival with the facades of the theatres visible above the heads of the people. Several general shots, and then the theatre curtain, which was raised at the beginning of the second half, slowly descends.*